KUNWINJKU BIM

Western Arnhem Land Paintings
from the collection of the Aboriginal Arts Board

Annemarie Brody

National Gallery of Victoria
7 December 1984 — 24 June 1985

This exhibition is proudly sponsored by

Published by the National Gallery of Victoria,
180 St Kilda Road, Melbourne, 1984

Brody, Annemarie, 1948-.
Kunwinjku bim.

Bibliography.
ISBN 0 7241 0104 7.

1. Australia Council. Aboriginal Arts Board - Catalogs. 2 . Aborigines,
Australian — Northern Territory — Arnhem Land — Painting —
Exhibitions. I. National Gallery of Victoria. II. Title.

759.01'1

Editor: Judith Ryan
Designer: Kathy Richards
Photographer: Sue McNab
Typesetter: Janet Brady
Printer: Cambec Press Pty Ltd

Cover illustration: cat.26
KANDAKID:PLAINS KANGAROO
by Bob Balirrbalirr Dirdi
90 x 69

FOREWORD

SPONSOR'S MESSAGE

The National Gallery of Victoria places great significance on the opening of its new gallery of Aboriginal and Oceanic art. Appropriately, the first year's program for this gallery will exclusively present Aboriginal art. The Gallery is pleased to be devoting a newly designed permanent space for the display of Aboriginal art and the art of Pacific cultures. Under its new program, the Gallery will place special emphasis on bringing to the attention of the general public those qualities of vitality and renewal so strongly evident in Aboriginal aesthetic traditions.

The Gallery is deeply indebted both to the Aboriginal Arts Board of the Australia Council which has generously loaned the contemporary works in the exhibition and to the Museum of Victoria, for its willingness to lend a select group of rare paintings from its historical collection. All galleries depend crucially on the support and enthusiasm of the private sector for developing special projects. This exhibition has been made possible by Mazda who has enthusiastically come forward to sponsor 'A Year of Aboriginal Art in the National Gallery of Victoria'. Mazda has proven to be an exceptional corporate supporter of the arts, giving substantial financial assistance for a whole year's activity and we are deeply appreciative of the opportunity it has provided to present KUNWINKJU BIM, the first of an exciting series of exhibitions on Aboriginal art.

Patrick McCaughey
Director

Mazda is proud to sponsor 'A Year of Aboriginal Art in the National Gallery of Victoria'. It gives us particular pleasure that this year of Aboriginal art coincides with the one hundred and fiftieth anniversary of the State of Victoria and the twenty-fifth anniversary of Mazda's operations in Australia. Mazda believes that public corporations have a responsibility to support those community activities which benefit all Australians. It takes pride and pleasure in the knowledge that it has created a new program at the National Gallery of Victoria. Mazda hopes that the Victorian community will enjoy and be stimulated by KUNWINJKU BIM, the first of a series of three exhibitions comprising 'A Year of Aboriginal Art'.

Malcolm Gough
General Manager
Mazda Motors

CONTENTS

Western Arnhem Land Escarpment
Photo. R. Morrison

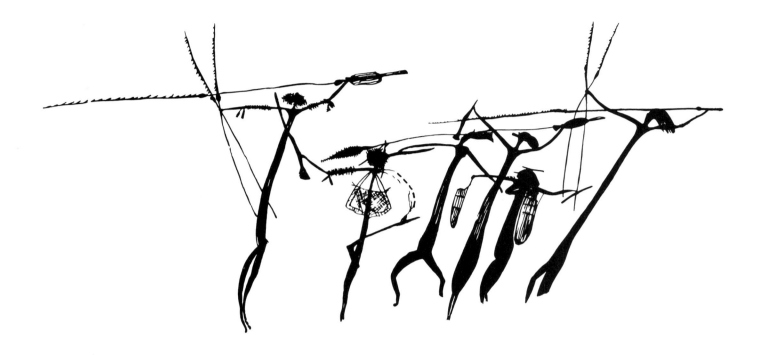

Rock paintings
Human beings in 'late' Mimi style
Deaf Adder Creek area, Mt Gilruth, Site 7
Brandl 1982:fig.91

NOTE ON THE EXHIBITION

In 1974, the Aboriginal Arts Board acquired a major collection of Oenpelli paintings from the Anglican Church Missionary Society's Sydney gallery. In 1977, fifty-two of these paintings went on tour to major centres in Australia and Europe in the exhibition 'Oenpelli Paintings on Bark'. Two years later, in 1979, the Aboriginal Arts Board published *Oenpelli Bark Paintings* which illustrated and documented a larger selection of works from their collection. KUNWINJKU BIM comprises the 1977 exhibition collection with a further selection of eight paintings from the same period. Also included in the exhibition are two groups of paintings which provide an interesting historical perspective on the contemporary works: five of these, collected by Spencer and Cahill, at Oenpelli circa 1912, have been generously loaned by the Museum of Victoria and the remaining five, collected by Mountford circa 1948 are from the Gallery's own collection.

On this occasion the earlier exhibition has been retitled in order to focus attention on the artists, all Kunwinjku language speakers. This change of focus is not intended to diminish the significance of Oenpelli as the place where the artists produced these works at a particular period — that era in the late 60s and early 70s when Oenpelli was both a centre and synonym for the western Arnhem land painting style. Rather, it is to direct attention to the importance of the Kunwinjku people and their art within a wider context. Today, artists who live in those regions marked by Croker and Goulburn Islands in the north, the Tomkinson River in the east, Bamyili and Katherine in the south, and Oenpelli in the west all share certain painting characteristics which distinguish a western Arnhem Land style and the men who produce these paintings often come together to perform ceremonies and can speak or hear the Kunwinjku language (cf. Taylor 1982:24).

Kunwinjku denotes the cultural-linguistic group to which the artists belong. The spelling used is that adopted by the Oenpelli people. An alternative form of spelling, Gunwinggu, is also commonly used. *Bim* is the Kunwinjku term for painting.

Pronunciation: *Kun-winj-ku* (the nj sound has no English equivalent but approximates to the ng sound in singing).

ACKNOWLEDGEMENTS

I most gratefully acknowledge the generous advice and assistance of the following people in the preparation of this catalogue: Peter Carroll, who was closely involved in the original documentation of the Aboriginal Arts Board's collection acquired through the Church Missionary Society's Sydney gallery and directly from the Oenpelli artists, for his assistance in matters relating to Kunwinjku language and culture; Peter Cooke for advice and discussion about the exhibition and for providing additional biographical information on the artists; Jennifer Isaacs, who wrote the catalogue text of the previous exhibition for discussions about the earlier project, additional information and advising on a further selection of paintings. I would particularly like to thank Luke Taylor for making available his paper 'Dreaming Transformations in Gunwinggu Bark Paintings', presented to the A.I.A.S. Biennial Conference 'Aboriginal Arts in Contemporary Australia' (1984) and for many generous and informative discussions about the paintings. I also wish to thank Chris Fondum and Merv Donovan, Project Officers, Aboriginal Arts Board, for their assistance and co-operation and Geoffrey Burke, Assistant Curator, Special Projects, National Gallery of Victoria, for valued assistance in the course of preparing the exhibition.

I am deeply indebted to David McCabe of Robin Wade Design Associates (Australia) Pty Ltd for creating a wonderful new space for KUNWINJKU BIM and future exhibitions of Aboriginal and Oceanic art in the National Gallery of Victoria.

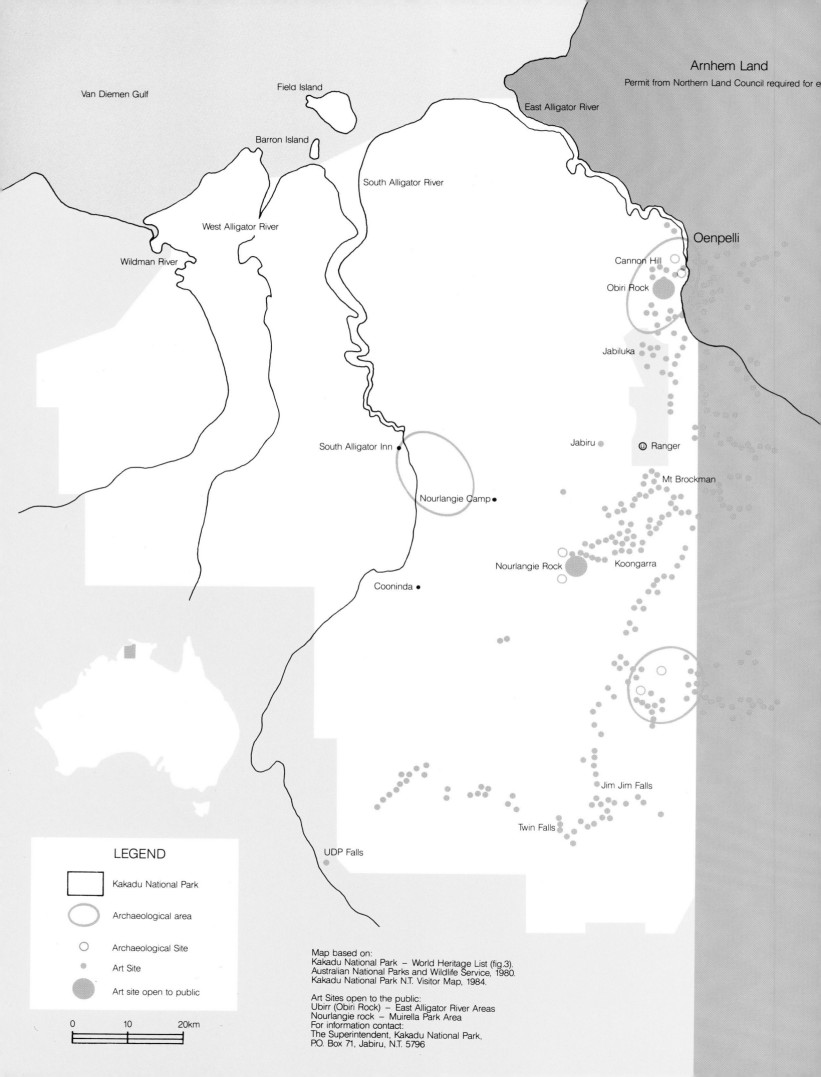

Van Diemen Gulf

Field Island

Barron Island

Arnhem Land
Permit from Northern Land Council required for e

East Alligator River

South Alligator River

West Alligator River

Oenpelli

Wildman River

Cannon Hill

Obiri Rock

Jabiluka

South Alligator Inn

Jabiru

Ⓤ Ranger

Mt Brockman

Nourlangie Camp

Nourlangie Rock

Koongarra

Cooninda

Jim Jim Falls

Twin Falls

UDP Falls

LEGEND

Kakadu National Park

Archaeological area

○ Archaeological Site

• Art Site

Art site open to public

Map based on:
Kakadu National Park – World Heritage List (fig.3).
Australian National Parks and Wildlife Service, 1980.
Kakadu National Park N.T. Visitor Map, 1984.

Art Sites open to the public:
Ubirr (Obiri Rock) – East Alligator River Areas
Nourlangie rock – Muirella Park Area
For information contact:
The Superintendent, Kakadu National Park,
P.O. Box 71, Jabiru, N.T. 5796

0   10   20km

INTRODUCTION

For the city dweller on the urban fringes of Australia, Kakadu National Park will possibly come to represent all that is exotic about the 'top end' of the continent – a remote, beautifully varied, dramatic tropical wilderness. Kakadu encompasses a stunning and diverse topography – tidal flats, lowlands, floodplains, escarpment and outliers. Rock art sites are densely concentrated in this region where the East Alligator River forms a natural border between Kakadu National Park and Arnhem Land. This western margin of the vast Arnhem Land Plateau rises steeply, 300 metres high in places, in sandstone cliffs that have been relentlessly eroded and weathered into a landscape of deep ravines and fantastically sculptured rock formations. Here, within Kakadu and on the Oenpelli side, in Arnhem Land, Aboriginal societies over millennia passed the wet season in the sheltered grandeur of the escarpment and its outliers. A magnificent legacy of their seasonal occupation remains in over a thousand galleries of rock art which form 'perhaps the oldest and most significant expressions of human creativity' (Chaloupka 1983a:3). The universal importance of this region was recognized in 1981 when Kakadu National Park became one of few areas to be accepted on the World Heritage List.

Rock art, from beginnings conservatively estimated around 25,000 (B.P.), consisted of both naturalistic and narrative images. Inferences based on changes in style and imagery in this visual record, and archaeological and environmental evidence, have provided a broad outline of cultural, ecological and technological change in the Aboriginal world of western Arnhem Land. As such, it 'constitutes the longest historical record of any group of people' (ibid.:5). In the first claim to be heard under the *Aboriginal Land Rights (N.T.) Act* in 1976, the area of the park – in former times closely settled by clans belonging to no less than seven language groups – was returned to the descendants of the traditional owners (ibid.:3). Chaloupka (1983B:15) has written an impressionistic account of life in this region:

Members of a given clan are spiritually linked to a specific territory which encompasses a number of features and sites where the mythic beings, during the creation period of the Dreaming, performed a certain act, left a part of themselves, or remained at the end of that period. Within each clan's territory there is at least one site which represents the life essence of a particular species. The traditional owners of the land carry out appropriate rituals at each of these centres which ensure the distribution of the species across the land. Thus, the Warramal were responsible for Guluban djang which contains the life essence of the black flying fox *(Pteroptus alecto)*. They enacted their ritual at this site and called out the names of locales and territories where this species should prosper. The clans were interdependent and sharing communities. They hunted and collected food and resources over one another's territory, sharing the seasonal bounty of a particular area. Through their travels they knew intimately large areas of land, their spiritual bases, the dreamings and the sacred and dangerous sites, and in their presence behaved accordingly.

The most tragic and dramatic effect of contact on the Aboriginal societies of the 'top end' was the severe reduction of their populations (cf. Keen 1980) and the displacement and movement of people away from their traditional lands towards European settlements. Oenpelli was the first such settlement in western Arnhem Land and later became the major population centre in the region. In 1976, some sixty years after Paddy Cahill, a buffalo shooter, first established a dairy, orchard and garden by the Oenpelli Lagoon, and the long period from 1925 during which the settlement was the responsibility of the Anglican Church Missionary Society, Oenpelli became an Aboriginal township, administered by the Gunbalanya Council under the Northern Land Council.

When Sir Baldwin Spencer visited Cahill's settlement at Oenpelli in 1912, on an official enquiry into the life and culture of its people, the population was mainly Kakadu – whose numbers were later tragically to decline. Later evidence suggests that Spencer's 'Kakadu nation' undoubtedly included a number of different groups living in the area. During Land Rights discussions at Oenpelli in the 1970s, the older men were adamant that Kakadu country lay on the western side of the East Alligator River and near the mouth of the south Alligator River and that the Kakadu people had only come to the Oenpelli area with Cahill (cf. AAB 1979:18). The traditional lands of the Kunwinjku people lay to the east and south-east of Oenpelli, around Tor Rock in the west and the plateau country to the south (Berndt 1970:9). The Kunwinjku presence at Oenpelli dates from the 20s but by the late 40s the Oenpelli population had become and remained predominantly Kunwinjku. In the early 1970s, as part of a widespread 'outstation movement', some Kunwinjku groups seeking to re-establish their cultural autonomy reversed the pattern of the past and moved away from Oenpelli back to their traditional lands. Today, Aboriginal people in the Alligator Rivers region live amidst the *realpolitik* and social consequences of what Tatz (1982:122) has referred to as 'this complex set of incongruities' – the triadic relationship between people, sacred sites and uranium.

State borders, maps of exploration, roads and mining leases – the accumulating routes and territories of recent Australian society – inexorably overlaid a very different and complex Aboriginal map of origins and occupancy. Based on a precise and intense relationship to land held sacred to the presence, law and memory of Dreaming Ancestors, Aboriginal culture constitutes a sense of absolute and eternal belonging. Those riches, cultural and natural, which make Kakadu in particular and western Arnhem Land in general, of supreme value in the contemporary world possess another history, 'inside' and prior to the perspectives brought by western cultural values. Rock art, paintings on bark, body painting, ceremonial objects, song, dance and oral history – unified in the theatre of major ceremonies – constitute in different ways an Aboriginal history of western Arnhem Land. It is through such rich and diverse aesthetic traditions that Aboriginal law, science, religious thought and economic rationale – formally segregated in industrial societies – are integrated, indivisible and renewed.

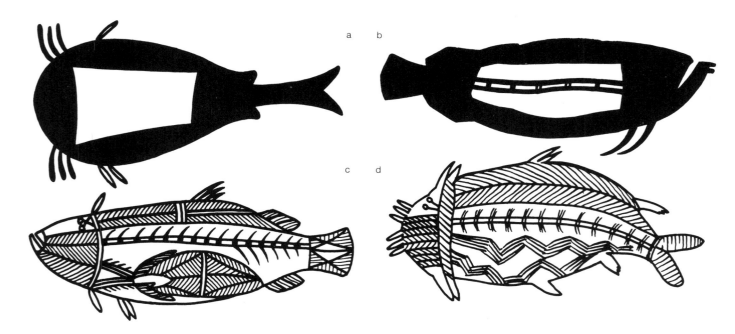

Typology of x-ray art, on the example of fish designs:
(a) incipient; (b) simple; (c) standard;
(d) complex x-ray art
Brandl 1982:fig.51

Rock painting
A complex composition with a yam figure in a long head-dress holding a Rainbow
Snake and a yam string encircling additional yam figure
Chaloupka 1983A:fig.1.6 (f)

ROCK ART

For thousands of years, painting on rock has been an integral part of western Arnhem Land cultural traditions. The works of contemporary Kunwinjku painters on bark reveal continuities and innovations with the art of the rock faces which in itself shows fascinating sequences of stylistic change. The transient medium of painting on bark does not survive in the archaeological record, but this art, along with body painting is considered to have been practised since early prehistory. Commenting on the accomplished draughtsmanship of human figures in prehistoric rock art styles, Chaloupka (1983a:8) writes that the forms presuppose 'a long development of such tactile skills, perhaps in other media such as drawing in sand or on bark'.

Artists were painting on rock and bark when Spencer was at Oenpelli in 1912. At Inlayak Hill a residual of the Arnhem Land Plateau, he remarked that:

The most interesting things, and what we came up to see, were the rock-shelters of the natives...where they rest in the cool of the evening during the wet season, when the flats below are transformed into swamps. The shelters were overhung with shelving rocks all round the top of the hill, so that they could change their camps to suit the changing weather. If the winds and rain blew in from the north, all they had to do was to pick up their few belongings and take their fire-sticks round to the shelters on the south side. The shelters were indeed such that they could accommodate themselves to any kind of weather.

The slanting roofs and sides were one mass of native drawings, precisely similar to those done on bark, but, here, the rocks had been blackened for long years by the smoke of countless campfires and the drawings, most of them fishes, had been superimposed on one another, the brighter colours of the more recent ones standing out clearly on the dark background. Here and there were groups of stencilled hands and feet. On other rock shelters along the Alligator River the drawings were not superimposed and comprised fishes, turtles, crocodiles and snakes. Very rarely there was a drawing...that represented a gnome-like creature. (Spencer 1928:823-4).

The first detailed survey of rock art sites was undertaken by the 1948 American-Australian Scientific Expedition to Arnhem Land led by Dr C.P. Mountford who also collected and described a large group of Oenpelli paintings on bark (Mountford 1956). He identified two widely differing styles which he broadly defined as *polychrome x-ray* for those variously coloured paintings in which internal anatomical details and skeletal structure are depicted and *monochrome mimi* for the single colour human figure style. He noted that the range of subjects and manner of depicting them in *x-ray* style was limited: 'birds, fish and animals, but seldom man, being drawn in side elevation and reptiles in plan. Nor do the subjects of the X-ray artists show any movement. It is essentially a static art' (ibid.:112). He found that the *Mimi* artists had a 'feeling for composition and movement ... Their main subject was man in action, running, fighting and throwing spears' (ibid.). Mountford's classification was adopted by later writers in discussions of paintings on bark. Whilst the terms *Mimi* and *x-ray* draw attention to the key stylistic features in both art forms,

the way they are used tends to conflate the socio-cultural circumstances in which ancient art forms evolved historically yet retained significance and meaning in the living traditions of contemporary Aboriginal societies.

More recent studies of rock art styles have been largely concerned with establishing chronological sequences and refining the basic style terms *mimi* and *x-ray*. In a classic study, Brandl (1982) expanded the typology to include early and late *mimi* styles, a transitional phase from *mimi* to *x-ray* followed by a sequence of early, standard and complex *x-ray* types. He also described subtle progressions and overlaps between these styles. Brandl was faced with the problem of inadequate scientific dating techniques in attempting to establish an accurate chronology for paintings which often appear as dense friezes of superimposed images quite difficult to disengage into sequences. He commented that his 'labels' serve 'the sole purpose of reporting categories of paintings which have a number of common characteristics. "Old" and "recent" refer to mimi art and x-ray art respectively usually when there is insufficient evidence to apply more precise terms' (ibid.:172).

In a fascinating account, which remains speculative to some extent, Chaloupka (1983a) radically extended the formalist approach to rock art style and chronology. His work unifies a range of insights into aesthetic, environmental and related socio-cultural change in western Arnhem Land. Adopting the methods of the art historian and archaeologist, Chaloupka analysed assemblages of style in their stratigraphic context and concluded that 'certain subjects of fauna and flora, of material culture and also mythological beings, were present in some styles and absent in others (ibid.:6). He further extended the significance of these findings by relating the stylistic and contextual periods he established to 'chronological indices available from climatological, geomorphological, archaeological and historical data for the region (ibid.). Further insights were obtained from the zoological and botanical sciences.

This combined aesthetic and scientific approach provided Chaloupka with a sequential framework which divided the chronological record into four periods with associated art styles – pre-estuarine, estuarine, freshwater and contact – spanning from 35,000 (B.P.) to the historical era. Whilst these periods do not represent a definitive chronology in the strict sense, an outline of Chaloupka's findings is provided below for the broad perspective it brings to matters of imagery and style in the overarching painting traditions of western Arnhem Land.

The key to this proposed schema lies in 'the environmental changes brought about by major sea level fluctuations during the late Pleistocene and early Holocene with the flooding of the Alligator River valleys, the subsequent development of tidal flats and saline plains and later their sedimentation with the creation of freshwater wetlands (ibid.:6).

Chaloupka proposes six art phases in the pre-estuarine period which he dates around 35,000 (B.P.). The earliest images were human handprints, imprints of grasses and thrown objects followed by a second phase in which animals and humans were represented in a naturalistic mode. Images of extinct megafauna also appear in their early style horizon. A third phase, recorded on 260 shelters extending across the Arnhem Land Plateau and its outliers, he called the 'dynamic figure style' – the *mimi* style of other writers – which 'consists of small, exquisite drawings of humans, anthropomorphs, and animals' singly or in narrative complexes characterized by expressive action. The image of a running male figure with widespread legs and forward thrust body has become an icon of the style (ibid.:8). Animals represented in this style include the echidna, wallaroos, thylacines, Tasmanian Devils, pythons, the long-necked turtle and freshwater fish. Chaloupka suggests that the portrayal of animal-headed beings represents 'the first evidence of mythogenesis in the rock art of this region' (ibid.:10). In the fourth style, 'post dynamic' and the fifth 'simple figures with boomerangs' the expressive action of the earlier style gave way to frontal static images and increasing schematization of form. The last phase of this period, the 'yam figures' involved a conceptual change to symbolic representation which, Chaloupka speculates, reflected changes in the artists' psychological environment. Citing Mulvaney (1975) 'who suggested that the loss of large areas of land arising within some human generations required adaptive efforts and a conciliatory philosophy' he links the emergence of new mythologies to the rising of the seas and the attendant dislocation of local populations (ibid.:12).

Chaloupka proposes a connection between the appearance of yams and the Rainbow Snake as major subjects in this style and the changed environment – suggesting that the yam symbolism might derive from prior contact with New Guinea peoples. He observes that in northern myths the Rainbow Snake is asociated with rain and floods and in coastal variations emerges from the sea and swallows or drowns people (ibid.). He describes the style as:

That of a knobbed yam tuber with a number of vines, or strings, evolving in time into a phytomorphic being and finally a man. The style motif of the yam, its physiognomy, was also transposed over that of a turtle, flying fox, birds, a number of zoomorphs and the Rainbow Snake. These are assembled with the 'yam people' in involved compositions...The Rainbow snake, not portrayed in previous rock art styles, became the second most depicted subject in the yam figure styles. As the myths associated with this being are still related today and as the Rainbow Snake still continues to play a major part in the ritual of this region, its representation in this early rock art style and its portrayal in the subsequent styles documents this as the world's longest continuing religious belief (ibid.:11).

The estuarine period, in Chaloupka's schema, begins with the 'first appearance of paintings representing the animal species introduced into the region with the flooding of the Alligator River valleys by the post-glacial rise in sea level between 7,000 and 9,000 years ago' (ibid.:12). In this period, he found a return to naturalistic modes of representation which develop into the x-ray style. He states that the painting convention of the x-ray style 'involved a complete reversal of the sequence and method of pigment application used in previous styles, when the majority of paintings were line constructs in red, in which white or yellow pigments were used only in emphasizing their outline and as additional decoration'

(ibid.:13). X-ray painting, he classified into descriptive and decorative phases with anatomical realism being replaced in some paintings by decorative hatching. Although paintings in the x-ray style predominate in this period, 'other forms of depiction are common and in time may be grouped into definite styles'. Chaloupka comments that 'it is possible that when several styles appear contemporaneously, they may have been used for different purposes and functions' (ibid.:14).

Depictions of new species such as the magpie goose and its hunters equipped with specialized goose spears appear in the freshwater period, some 1,000 years ago when 'freshwater billabongs and paperbark (*Malaleuca* spp.) swamps developed over the previously saline plains' (ibid.). There are also images of women poling their paperbark rafts into the wetlands to collect goose eggs. The majority of paintings in this and the contact period which followed are executed in the x-ray style. The seasonal trading visits of the Macassans to the coast of northern Australia, their ships and items of material culture, such as a sheathed *kris* depicted in x-ray style, are recorded in rock art. Out of the images of European presence – paintings of ships, early explorers, the construction of the railway to the Pine Creek goldfields, Darwin's wharf of the 1890s, buffalo shooters, a portrait of the first missionary and the sorcery images arising from the social havoc of introduced diseases – one could reconstruct a history of European settlement of the north (ibid:15).

Prior to European contact, the survival of rock paintings frequently exposed to environmental damage, was not the critical matter for concern that it has become since the radical curtailment of clan life and the passing of the indigenous artists and custodians. Edwards (1979:126) has written that 'constant painting in occupation shelters and re-touching of sacred designs ensured a continuing body of superb art'. Chaloupka ties the decline of rock art to the social effects of contact, that 'people who went to live on missions and settlements chose to use the alternative form of bark painting, itself of long tradition, to depict subjects previously painted on the walls of shelters, and this then became the dominant art form of the region' (ibid.:15). Although the traditional importance of rock art was eroded by contact individual artists continued to paint occasional designs when visiting their countries (ibid.). The last-known painting in the x-ray tradition was executed by Najombolmi when:

In 1964, only a year before his death, he camped for the last time in this shelter. By then he had witnessed the impact of European contact on Aboriginal sociocultural systems elsewhere in the Northern Territory, and now he saw changes happening within his own region. Bridges began to span the rivers, which were the actual barriers in the past, and each year an increasing number of outsiders were intruding into his land. He thought of the people who used to live here, and of the Dreaming. In his swag he carried ochres which he had collected on his travels. He took them out, prepared the pigments and painted the people back into the shelter. There are two family groups, men standing amidst their wives, some of whom he depicted with milk in their breast, as if he really wished them to be alive, to procreate and to people the land again. He built a platform and from this he painted the mythic beings, Namargon, the Lightning Man and his wife Bargini, and Namondjolk, a malignant spirit. This painted wall is unique, the last work of a great artist (Chaloupka 1983b:22).

Binin (people) and Mythic Beings
Anbangbang Shelter, Nourlangie Rock
by Najombolmi, 1964
Photo. R. Morrison

39. NAMARRKON : THE LIGHTNING SPIRIT, AND THE WARDBUKARRA – WARDBUKARRA

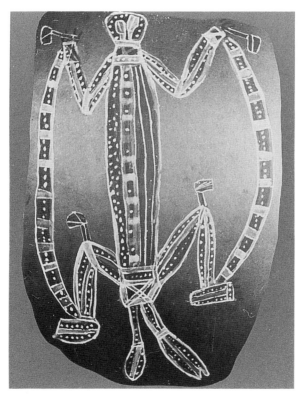

Lightning Spirit
Earth pigments on paper
Oenpelli c.1948
Photo: courtesy South Australian Library
Mountford-Sheard Collection

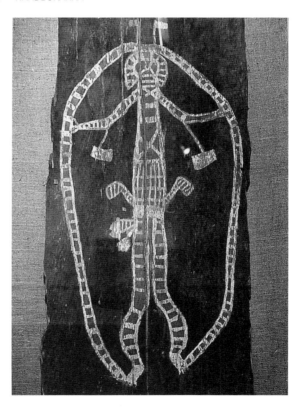

v. LIGHTNING SPIRIT

THE PAINTINGS

Kunwinjku knowledge of the western Arnhem Land environment that has sustained their people over millennia is reflected on many levels: in their taxonomies of natural species; on an economic plane through hunting and gathering strategies and the management of natural resources; and in the symbolic domain through a religious philosophy and its material expression in myth, ritual and art. Kunwinjku life is directly concerned with the country and all it contains; with the fertility of the land and the seasonal cycle that brings about renewal and diversity. Their mythology provides a rich vein of oral history and carries within its epic sagas of creation and discovery an enormous amount of practical information concerning topography, natural resources and social relations. Images of people, animals, plants, marine creatures and spiritual beings are part of a densely structured cosmography which unifies the relationships between man and all other creation in a single order whose foundations were established by the Nayuhyungi, the First People, in the creative era known as the Dreaming.

Many Kunwinjku paintings and their associated myths relate to ceremonies and ritual that are of a restricted sacred. nature and are therefore not included in the exhibition. The sixty paintings in KUNWINJKU BIM deal with various aspects of traditional life in an 'open' context: they portray plants and animals, Ancestors in human and animal form, spirit beings such as the Mimi, Dreaming events and secular subjects from everyday life. Some paintings are single iconic images, essentially static in form, whilst others depict scenes of collective action: hunting, food gathering, dancing and the holding of ceremonies. Myths and stories are included to elucidate the images.

The first part of the exhibition (cat.1–27) mainly comprises paintings of fauna and flora. Whilst some belong to the more secular realm of hunting and gathering, others are decorated with *rarrk* patterning, or clan designs, which denote their totemic significance as manifestations of the shape-changing Ancestors who founded the Kunwinjku world.

Artists generally place a strong emphasis on the accurate delineation of natural species, noting for example, that 'a hill kangaroo is characterized by heavy front legs and an antillopine kangaroo by more gracile front legs' (Taylor 1984). Mythology may also have an important bearing on the representation of species: 'The features which it is important to show in a figurative painting are usually the subject of myth... [and] may deal with such subjects as why the hill kangaroo has heavier shoulders than the antillopine kangaroo' (ibid.). Myths and rituals 'provide a cultural explanation for the observed body features of natural species and provide the rationale for painting those features in particular ways' (ibid.). Kunwinjku attention to the differentiation of natural species in art is not therefore a straightforward matter of empirical observation. Because of a shared affinity, in the Kunwinjku view, between particular social groups and particular natural species (a relationship often referred to as totemic) the aesthetic distinctions conventionalized in paintings also serve to differentiate among species in the natural world and social

groups in the cultural world (cf. ibid.). As such ritually important images are owned by clans, religious in origin and emblematic of socio-cultural identity, mistakes in representation may amount to more than a failure of perception or skill and artists who make errors in these contexts may be subject to ritual fines.

Whilst many Kunwinjku paintings are vibrant with naturalistic detail, especially when compared with the more abstract forms of other style areas, they are nevertheless highly conventionalized images. As most of the artists in KUNWINJKU BIM are represented by several works, and there are some of the same subject (most notably a fine series of kangaroos), the viewer is afforded an opportunity to appreciate different approaches to image construction in Kunwinjku painting: to examine the ways in which a tradition-orientated visual language is susceptible to highly individual treatment in form, colour and patterning: and is a pictorially dynamic means of expressing Kunwinjku realities in images of intense clarity and power.

1. NJALGAN : ARCHER FISH

4. THE FATE OF THE GREEDY FISHERMAN

2. NAMARNKOL : BARRAMUNDI

6. DADBE AND NGARDERRWO : TWO SNAKES AND A TORTOISE

5. KUMOKEN : CROCODILES

7. KAWALAN : GOANNAS

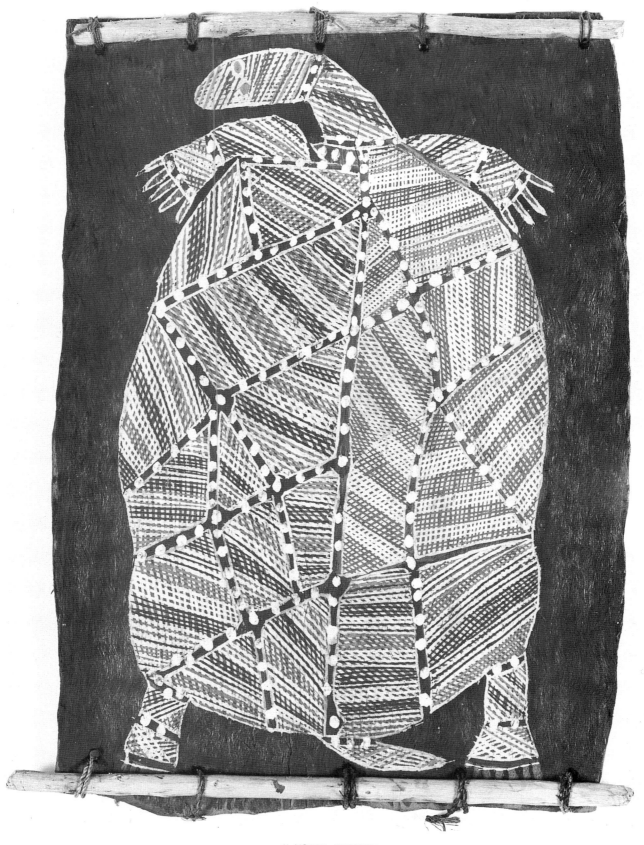

11. NGARD : TORTOISE

12. NAWARAN : ROCK PYTHON

9. HUNTER AND DEAD KANGAROO

10. NGARRBEK : ECHIDNA

8. DUKULA AND LAMBALK : POSSUMS FEEDING

14. BENUK : BUSH TURKEY

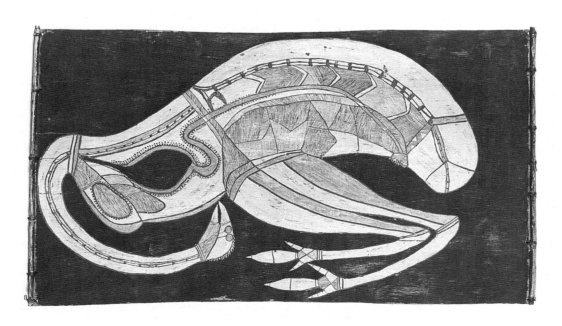

13. NGURRUDU : EMU

30

15. KARRBADA : LONG YAM

17. MANMARNAWAN : BUSH FRUIT

16. YAM

21. KARURRKEN : PLAINS KANGAROO

27. THREE RAINBOW SNAKES

28. NGALYOD IN HER WATERHOLE

30. NGALYOD AND THE SACRED TREE

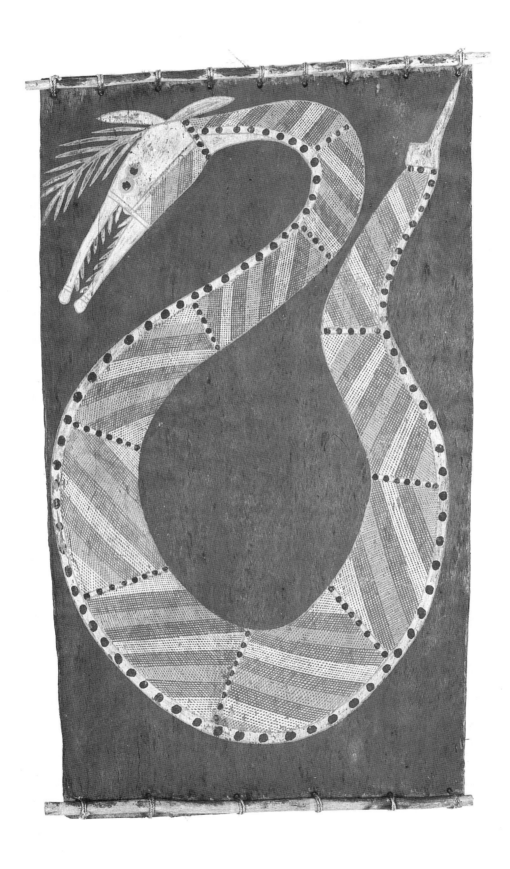

29. NGALYOD

34. NGALYOD AND NGALKUNBURRIYAYMI

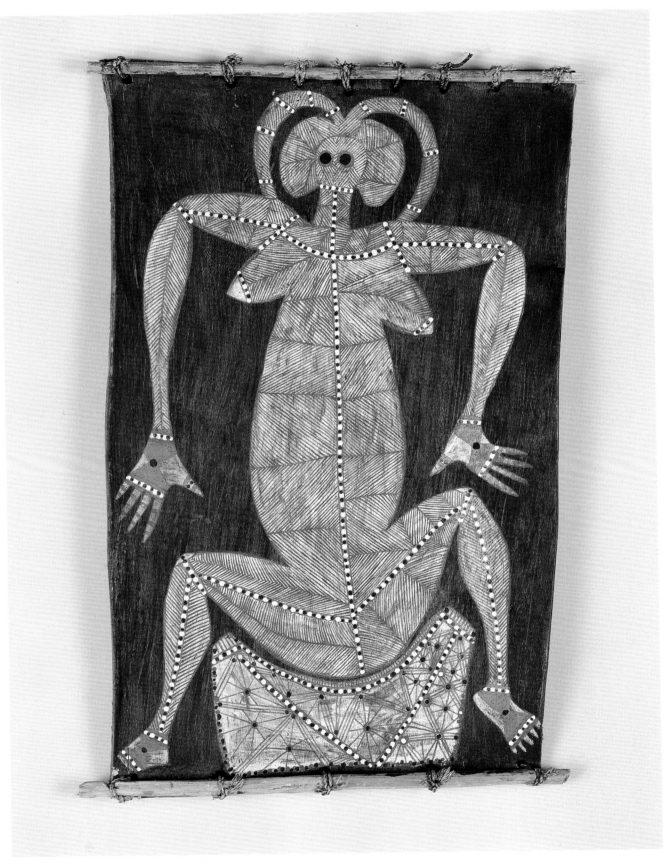

35. NGALKUNBURRIYAYMI : THE FEMALE SPIRIT

31. NGALYOD

33. BORLUNG

37. NAMARRKON : THE LIGHTNING SPIRIT

45. LUMA LUMA

47. NGALDJORLBOH, THE SPIRIT WOMAN

48. NAMORRORDRDO SPIRITS

44. KUNBUDJURRI, CEREMONIAL LEADER OF THE UBAR

46. LIKANAYA AT HER SACRED WATERHOLE

52. EVIL SPIRIT OR DEVIL

51. WAKEWAKEN SPIRIT

53. EVIL SPIRIT OR DEVIL

49. NAWONGBERD AND HIS FOUR WIVES

50. WAYARRA : EVIL SPIRITS AND KULUBAN:FLYING FOXES IN THEIR CAVE

56. MIMI SPIRITS

57. MIMI SPIRIT AND KANGAROO DANCING

58. MIMI HUNTER AND FEEDING KANGAROO

THE ARTISTS

Apart from the small group of Oenpelli paintings collected by Spencer and Cahill circa 1912 and those by Mountford in 1948, KUNWINJKU BIM represents the work of thirteen artists working at Oenpelli between 1968 and 1974. Aboriginal languages have no special terms which approximate to western categories of 'art' and 'artist', although there are words, such as *bim* in Kunwinjku, which denote painting. The role of 'artist', that is, one who creates works for an external, largely anonymous art public, is a recent specialization in Arnhem Land reflecting one aspect of social change in the region. All men in traditional Aboriginal society (and in some cases women) produced paintings and, whilst individual talent and skill were recognized, there was no separate occupational class of artists as is commonly found in other cultures. Whilst art was principally the domain of men, in some societies women either exclusively owned designs or could acquire the right to paint designs that belonged to men. Among the Kunwinjku, as in western and central Arnhem Land generally, women on the whole do not produce paintings, 'not even assisting their husbands and brothers with the infill [cross-hatching] on bark paintings made for sale (Morphy 1981:58).

The principal artists in this exhibition were, or are, senior men in Kunwinjku society. Six of these men: Bob Balirrbalirr Dirdi, Spider Namirrkgi Nabunu, Anchor Barbuwa Wurrkgidj, Paddy Nadamjorle Maralngurra, Namerredje Guymala and Yuwunyuwun Marruwarr died in the 1970s and Jimmy Nakkurridjdjilmi Nganjmira in 1982. Whilst most of these artists spent significant periods of their lives at Oenpelli in the 60s and 70s they also maintained close ties with their clan lands, either based there or returning for long periods. In the Artists' Biographies (p.78) the clan, subsection and country of each artist are given, as kinship and territorial affilations are at the heart of Kunwinjku life and art.

In the course of the 1970s, many artists returned permanently to their clan estates (more appropriately seen as a series of interrelated places or Dreaming sites than a set of formal boundaries) as part of the 'outstation' movement in which clan-based communities again became the primary focus of Aboriginal values and traditions. This movement involved an increase in religious activities and a renewal and intensification of the spiritual bonds of the artists and their children with their totemic landscape. In these small communities, the sale of art to overseas and urban Australian audiences has become a significant source of income in economies which, in some instances are still largely based on hunting and gathering. The sale of art has had no negative effects on the value of art in traditional contexts where it has remained integral to ceremonial life (cf. Morphy ibid.:54). The strong cultural traditions that prevailed amongst the Kunwinjku community at Oenpelli in the 60s and 70s persist today and for Taylor (1982:25) 'the fact that [Kunwinjku] people are still painting sacred designs for ceremonies and are still visiting rock art sites, suggests that artists will continue to produce an art that is meaningful in the context of western Arnhem Land culture'.

Whilst the artists in the exhibition were able to devote a considerable amount of their time to painting at Oenpelli in the late 60s (in part a response to the Church Missionary Society's program to market their art, cf.AAB 1979:49), it is more often the case that subsistence and ceremonial commitments compete for the time that men have available for painting.

Altman (1982:15) writes that Kunwinjku men may gain status in three main ways: 'by being good hunters; by being good *bisnis* (ceremony) men; and by being good artists (or artisans)'. Whilst they are young, Kunwinjku men are expected to concentrate on excelling in the subsistence and ritual domains; as they get older, and semi-retire from hunting activities, they have more free time to devote to painting. Young men (twenty-five to thirty-five) may become major artists but they also tend to excel among their peers in hunting and ritual activities as well as in the ceremonial domain (cf. ibid.). Art production generally tends to increase in the wet season when people's mobility is restricted and there are few competing ceremonial commitments. The dry season marks the commencement of the annual ceremonial cycle which can also entail heavy economic commitments in the form of provisioning the large gatherings of participants. Cooke (1982:27) writes that 'it is not uncommon for ceremonies [which also provide a forum for wide-ranging discussions] to take six months or more to reach their conclusion' and 'that as many as 1,000 Aboriginal people from widely spread locations may be drawn to participate in the culmination of a ceremony.'

The major ceremonial cycles practised by the Kunwinjku are the *ubar*, the *madayin* (or *maraiin*) the *kunapipi* and the *yabaduruwa* – collective re-enactments of the epics of the Dreaming. Major ceremonies are the focal points of *rites de passage* or initiations which structure the progression of Kunwinjku boys from youth to manhood, to the ritual seniority which marks the deepest levels of knowledge of religious and cultural law in their society. It is primarily in the context of these ceremonies that young men are instructed by their fathers or ritual guardians in the execution and meaning of designs which play an integral role in the transmission of their religious heritage. Because the acquisition of painting skills and the knowledge of designs and their meanings is primarily gained through participation in ceremonies, there is necessarily a close link between status as a major artist and ritual seniority in Kunwinjku society. With age 'men gain access to a wider range of rights in designs and the confidence associated with ritual seniority to paint these designs in an open manner' (Altman ibid.:15).

In order to assume the social and ritual roles of their fathers, young men must develop an understanding of the complex mythological associations of their clan Dreaming sites (cf. Taylor 1984). On those occasions when a young artist receives instruction in painting, his father recounts the myths and descriptions of country associated with the subject. At the start of this 'apprenticeship', and particularly in relation to totemic images where accuracy is ritually important 'older artists usually complete the basic figure for younger artists by painting it as a white undercoat which the younger artist will then fill in with cross-hatching...a young artist may not be fully confident of these basic undercoats until he is fully advanced in his painting career' (ibid.). Young artists 'may learn to paint a design long before the full meaning of what he has painted is revealed to him in ceremony' (Taylor 1982:25).

Kunwinjku artists distinguish between figurative images infilled with x-ray features and those elaborated with *rarrk* patterns: 'Figures with x-ray motifs are associated with the secular realm of food sources and preparation or the hunting of animals, whereas a figure infilled with *rarrk* takes on ancestral overtones. Artists describe a kangaroo with x-ray features as "just a tucker kangaroo". Another with *rarrk* patterning will be described as "Dreaming kangaroo". Dreaming figures are associated with special meanings dramatised in sacred ritual' (ibid.:24). There is an emphasis on the correctness of Dreaming designs which typically have a more standardized formal content: '*Rarrk* must be painted in the correct sequences of colour and important details of mythological significance must be shown' (ibid.:25).

Possibly the most difficult images for a young artist to approach and master are the highly conceptual and creative paintings of the Dreaming which visually condense complex information about the totemic landscape: the Ancestors, their journeys and metamorphoses. The production of such paintings is fundamental to younger artists' understanding of the Dreaming in that they provide tangible images of esoteric and sacrosanct realities: 'Older artists, by virtue of their greater knowledge of myth and ritual and in some cases by their ability to see images of the Dreaming during magical experiences can confidently create painted images of the Dreaming' (Taylor 1984).

In Kunwinjku, as in other Aboriginal societies, aesthetic production is on the whole subject to ownership based on inheritance. Whilst artists have a wide range of designs they may paint, 'a few are more exclusively their own' (Taylor 1982:25). People inherit 'associations with the Dreaming Ancestors of their father's clan and these become their personal Dreamings. A man has the special right to paint the Dreamings of his own clan although he also has rights in the designs of his mother's and grandparent's clans' (ibid.). Taylor (1984) discusses an instance of artists who call a particular site 'mother' country and may therefore paint the figures of the owning clan because of 'their ceremonial association with the land.' In such cases, an artist is exercising his 'managerial' or *djunggai* role in relation to painting designs: 'whilst "owners" have an intrinsic spiritual link with their clan's ritual property, their sister's sons have a guardian or "managerial" role with respect to that property' (ibid.). One of the 'manager's' roles is to work at producing ceremonial artefacts for the owners on ritual occasions which also involves him in painting ceremonial designs on the bodies of the owners who will dance in the ritual (cf.Taylor 1984). The ownership and proper use of designs is protected by a system of ritual fines which may be imposed at ceremonial gatherings on an artist who has painted another man's Dreaming incorrectly or without his permission (cf.Taylor 1982:25). Whilst artists can exercise considerable latitude in painting secular subjects, there is an emphasis on ritual propriety in relation to Dreaming designs because they express the inviolable presence of the Dreaming Ancestors who first bestowed them on mankind.

PAINTING MATERIALS AND TECHNIQUES

The production of paintings on bark using a small range of natural materials – earth colours, fixatives, brushes and sheets of bark – involves meticulous skills in both the preparation of materials, and in the final execution of the painted image. Before contact, the traditional tools used to obtain and prepare barks were hand choppers, sharpened hardwood sticks and edge-ground stone axes (Edwards & Guerin 1969) but in recent times steel axes and knives have been used to trim barks and sandpaper is sometimes used to smooth the inner surface for painting (Altman 1982:14).

Seasonal factors have an important bearing on art and craft production in Arnhem Land, determining the availability of raw materials, subsistence activities, residence location, the ceremonial cycle, and the levels and range of artefacts produced for exchange (cf. ibid.:13). The Kunwinjku annual cycle 'is divided into six distinct seasons: three dry seasons (early dry or *yekkeh*, mid dry or *wurrgeng*, and late dry or *gurrung*) that run from about May to November; and three wet seasons (early wet or *gunumeleng*, mid wet or *gudjawk*, and late wet or *banggerreng*) that run from December to April (ibid.). The start of the dry season signals the commencement of the annual ceremonial cycle, which is 'loosely demarcated but regular' (ibid.). With the advent of the wet season, the tall, fast growing stringybark (*Eucalyptus tetrodonta*) becomes readily available and this is the best time for removing sheets of bark because the rising sap makes it supple and easy to strip. *Manyal-manyalk* (*Urena lobata*) from the bark of which bush strings are made, are also obtained during the wet and early dry seasons (ibid.). These are used to attach cross struts to bark paintings. Pigments and ochres tend to be collected over the dry season and stored for use over the wet seasons (ibid.).

PREPARATION OF THE BARKS

1. The artist selects a stringybark with a long straight trunk. With its first branches well up the trunk, the stringybark offers many feet of suitable bark which is checked for more obvious blemishes such as small knot-holes, splits or termite damage that might mar the painting surface.

2. Two horizontal incisions are made in the trunk according to the size of bark required. A vertical cut is made between these two points and the bark is ready to be gradually prized away with either the blade of an axe or a stick with its edge sharpened to a wedge. The artist is careful not to split or damage the bark in this process.

3. When removed, the bark is a hollow open cylinder, curled in the shape of the tree. It has a fine-grained, creamy-white inner layer: the rough outer layer is trimmed away.

4. The sheet of bark is then fired. Edwards & Guerin (1969) write that 'like many Aboriginal fires, this may seem to be a haphazard heap of rubbish. Deceptively so for their material

and arrangement are carefully judged to produce just the right temperature and type of heat for the task at hand. Dry leaves and grasses and smaller twigs are laid loosely over a base of tinder-dry sticks, spread evenly to take the full length of the bark. The sheet is placed on the fire outer side down, flattening quickly as the clear, hot flames drive the moisture out. A few handfuls of dry grass may be scattered over the bark to bring the flame to the top before the sheet is turned briefly to fire the inner side.' This firing also chars any superfluous bark making it easier to strip away.

5. After firing, the sheet is laid out flat on the ground and weighted with rocks or sand to prevent it from buckling and left in the open to season. Mountford (1956:13) notes that the drying process could take from several days to a fortnight depending on the humidity of the atmosphere.

6. Since the 1950s it has become standard practice to attach cross-sticks (against the grain of the bark) at either end of the painting to inhibit further movement. A series of holes is made along the ends of the bark and the struts are attached with bush string.

PIGMENTS

Ochres have always been highly prized possessions throughout Aboriginal Australia. Ludwig Leichardt and his party, the first Europeans to traverse the Alligator Rivers region, were made 'presents of red ochre which [the local people] seemed to value highly' (Edwards 1979:16). The natural ochres of red and yellow, white clay, black manganese and charcoal comprise the traditional palette of all Aboriginal art. McCarthy (1964:38) writes that 'extensive deposits of ochre like those at Yarrakinna in the Parachilna Ranges of South Australia, Wilgimia in Western Australia, in Arnhem Land and elsewhere, became centres of mythical and religious significance.' These pigments 'were traded and sought hundreds of miles away from the quarries, because it was believed that they possessed a mystical power through their having been created by particular ancestral spirit beings' (ibid.). Eastern Kunwinjku artists today obtain white pigment from a quarry which possesses great religious significance. The pigment which has been identified as Huntite, 98-99% pure calcium magnesium carbonate, is called *delek* in Kunwinjku. It is 'mined at a sacred (*djang*) site associated with the Rainbow Snake, Ngalyot. Eastern Gunwinggu [Kunwinjku] believe that the *delek*, in the form of nuggets, is the faeces of the snake. Mining is preceded by ritual calling to the deceased landowners and can only be undertaken during the dry season when Ngalyot sleeps. This white pigment is highly valued throughout the region and is traded for yellow ochres as far east as Gapuwiyak (Lake Evella). *Delek* is essential for bark painting and extremely important for body decoration in a wide range of ritual cult, mortuary and exchange ceremonies' (Altman 1982:13). In a more general comment on contemporary Arnhem Land art,

Morphy (1981:56) writes that the 'source of ochre may be important in ceremonial paintings, different shades of ochres having different religious connotations reflected in subtle aspects of their colour.' Pigments may also possess deep personal significance for an artist. Fox (1982:11) tells of an old Mangalili (east Arnhem Land) artist who placed before him three rocks (ochres) and some white clay (pigment): 'The red rock, he said, was his blood, the yellow rock his fat, the black rock his skin and the white clay his bones. These colours made up his palette. His eyes were full of gentleness and knowledge and his work reflected his state of mind.'

Mountford (1956:10) provides a detailed account of the source and use of pigments at Yirrkala and Oenpelli in 1948: 'At Yirrkala, the aborigines use four pigments, red, white, yellow, and black. The first two belong to the *dua* and the latter to the *jiritja* moiety. Red, *murngun*, and white, *kapun*, are plentiful in the cliffs at Yirrkala. It can however, be gathered only by the *dua* men who give it to those of the opposite moiety. Yellow, *kadangul*, and black, *tjunapul*, come from localities near Gurunga. The collection of the yellow pigments is associated with a ceremony in which men from the *jiritja* moiety only can take part. The *jiritja* distribute these pigments to the *dua* men.' At Oenpelli, he observed that most of the colours are obtained by trade: 'The best red ochre, *gunaitdai*, comes from a totemic place *Widitjan*, about eight days' journey south. If this ochre is in short supply, the aborigines use an inferior local ochre. For white, the aborigines use a stone, *outjain* (unidentified), which they first grind into a paste and, when it is partly dry, mould into small cakes. In this form the pigment is traded over long distances. The yellow ochre, *maragararum*, which is soft and easily ground, comes from some unidentified place to the far south.' Mountford did not gather any details about the source of the black, called *manmaijangarin* and considered it to be in short supply 'because it is rare in both the bark and cave paintings in the Oenpelli area' (ibid.).

Not all pigments are obtained through trade or ritual exchange; some may be freely gathered in the local environment. The suitability of pigments is judged by their purity, consistency and texture with some, for example, being more suited to body painting than painting on bark or rock (cf. Brandl 1983:106). White pigment is generally pipeclay, gypsum or natural chalk (kaolin); reds and yellows come from a variety of sources including oxides, haematite, ironstone and limonite. Blacks may be manganese or charcoal moistened with water (cf. Edwards & Guerin 1969). Brandl (ibid.) discusses in detail the pigments used by his western Arnhem Land artist informants. Concerning white pigment, they 'named two types of the same colour distinguished by their consistency: *barndja* or *woragid*, the "hard one", and *bi:m* or *gamununggu*, the "soft one". The first is dug or taken from sedimentary beds wherever they occur whilst the second is found in the moist ground of creek banks, above or below the water level' (ibid.). Yellow pigment can be found 'everywhere : usually it is taken from laterite beds or collected as worn pebbles in creeks'. In one deposit 'beds of bright yellow pigment occur between layers of kaolin and red ochre. The yellow ochre is apparently due to limonitic staining of the white kaolin' (ibid.). Both red and yellow ochres come in wide range of different shades. Red pigments are usually mined in quantity from natural deposits, collected as pebbles or found as inclusions in sandstone (ibid.). Brandl also discusses Aboriginal language terms for the pigments and comments on the classification of colours on the basis of their use in particular ritual contexts. The preparation of traditional paints, according to Kupka (1965:62), 'does not present any great problems. The painter leaves his coloured earths to soak in shells or other improvised containers; if they are too hard, he grinds them against stones, adding water until he obtains the desired paste.'

Both Spencer (1928:792) and Tindale (1926:117) observed that pigments were mixed to produce different shades of colouring, although Mountford commented that during his visits to Oenpelli, Yirrkala and Groote Eylandt in 1948, artists 'were not mixing their colours, the different pebbles of red and yellow ochres accounting for the varying shades of red and yellow in the paintings' (Mountford 1956:11). Tuckson (1964:66) writes that 'colours are not normally mixed, but are used directly so that their natural colour is retained, and with it a simply harmony.' Isaacs (AAB 1977:17) and Edwards & Guerin (1969) remark that colours are sometimes mixed to give a 'pink, orange or grey.'

FIXATIVES

As bark is extremely sensitive to changes in temperature and humidity and cleavages and flaking of paint are an inherent feature of the medium, fixatives are used to secure the paint surface. The early accounts of the use of fixatives describe them as being either applied directly to the surface of the painting to be painted or mixed in with the ground pigment but are not always precise. In recent decades, it has become common for commercial wood glue solutions to be used in lieu of traditional fixatives. The 1968-74 paintings in the exhibition make use of both kinds of fixative. Bush orchid sap (Isaacs pers. comm.) and the gum or resin from various localities were the common natural fixatives in use at Oenpelli (AAB 1977:17).

Elkin, Berndt & Berndt (1950:64) provide an interesting account of the application of natural fixatives in Arnhem Land in the late 1940s: 'if an artist is particularly anxious that his painting should not flake or powder unduly, he will add oil from a swamp root, similar to a miniature bamboo shoot. He does this by rubbing the flat stone with the shoot, and then mixing the ochre with water; the same shoot may also be used as a brush. Only a small amount of yellow or red ochre liquid is mixed at one time, so that throughout his drawing the artist is continually rubbing his lump of ochre and mixing his paints.' They further remark that in the case of black and white pigments 'as for the others, the oily bamboo shoot may be used to ensure the durability of the drawing' (ibid.:65).

Mountford (1956:11) gives a specific account of the use of fixatives in those areas of Arnhem Land he visited in 1948: 'The juice of one of the tree orchids (*Dendrobium* sp.) is used by the Arnhem-landers as a fixative on both bark and cave paintings. The orchid bulb is cut in halves, broken slightly by chewing, and in the Oenpelli and Yirrkala areas, rubbed directly on the surface of the bark or rock surface, or in Groote Eylandt, mixed with the colour on the grinding stone. This method of holding the colour is effective as long as pigments are applied thinly; if not they tend to flake off.' In a later publication, Mountford (1964:22), describes fixatives used on Melville Island: 'the gelatinous sap of one of the tree orchids, the wax and honey of the wild bee, well mixed together, and the yolks of the eggs of the sea-going turtle.' Elsewhere Mountford (1969:12) refers to'the wax of the stingless bee, well mixed with water, and the white of the eggs of the sea-going turtle.' In an overview of Arnhem Land bark paintings, Edwards & Guerin (1969) cite as fixatives 'the wax and honey of wild bees, the yolk of certain eggs and a preparation from chopped and boiled bloodwood leaves.' More recently, Morphy (1981:56) mentions two traditional fixatives: 'juices from the stem of a tree orchid or seagull's egg...'

The palettes or grindstones against which the pigments are ground are prized possessions of the artists and may be used for many years (Altman 1982 :14). Deeply patinated and weathered sandstone slabs containing grinding hollows have been found in situ in western Arnhem Land. Smaller portable grindstones impregnated with pigment have been dated to 18,000 years B.P. (Cooper et al 1981: cat.3 &4).

BRUSHES

These are the most specialized items of the artist's equipment (and are made in various sizes, shapes and materials). Most brushes are made from strips of stringybark or pliant green twigs — their ends frayed out by chewing to separate the fibres into bristles. Other specialized brushes are made from strands of human hair, feathers or leaf fibre bound at one end. An artist will often work with several brushes, each one suitable for a particular purpose.

Mountford (1956:12) describes three kinds of brushes normally used in Arnhem Land: a narrow strip of bark, chewed at one end used for broad lines: a cylindrical stick...about three inches long with a slightly burred end which the artist loads with colour and uses to make dots: and a third type made from a few fibres of palm leaf or a small feather, 'held delicately between the fingers and drawn away from the body.' This brush was used for the 'fine cross-hatching and lining in north-eastern Arnhem Land art, and the broken and parallel lines of Groote Eylandt.' Mountford noted that 'it is called *marait* by the Oenpelli people' (1981:56). He does not refer to human hair brushes which Morphy (ibid.:56) describes as consisting of 'a long strand of human hair bound to a thin stick. Such brushes are used to produce the thin lined, cross hatched infill characteristic of Arnhem Land painting. The brush is dipped into the pigment, then the hair laid on the painting before being drawn across the surface. In some areas, a feather or thin palm leaf rib is used instead of human hair.'

Whilst European brushes have been adopted in many parts of Arnhem Land, they are 'seldom used at Oenpelli where the artists firmly adhere to traditional techniques' (AAB 1977:17).

CATALOGUE ENTRIES

Media: All works are painted in earth pigments on stringybark with the exception of cat.vi-ix collected by Mountford, who supplied the artists from whom he commissioned works with 'sheets of rough-surfaced dark grey and green paper' when supplies of prepared bark became exhausted (Mountford 1956:13 fn.47) Measurements are given in cm, height before width.

Documentation has been primarily drawn from *Oenpelli Paintings in Bark*, Aboriginal Arts Board, 1977 and *Oenpelli Bark Paintings*, Aboriginal Arts Board, 1979. Documentation for six additional works (cat.16,30,40,42,48,53) included in this exhibition was provided by Luke Taylor, Department of Prehistory and Anthropology, Research School of Pacific Studies, A.N.U. Other sources are cited in the entries.

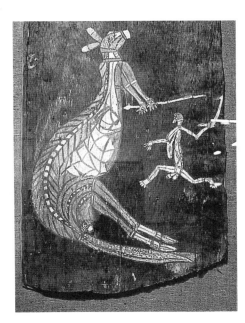

i.
KANGAROO AND HUNTER
Artist unknown
Group: Kakadu
Oenpelli, c.1912
127 x 81
Spencer Collection
Museum of Victoria

Spencer described this superb example of *x-ray* art as a 'life-size drawing of a very rare form of black kangaroo (*Macropus Woodwardi*) called Madjiborla, that lives amongst the Ranges and reaches a height of four feet' (Spencer 1928:809). The artist from whom Spencer acquired the painting told him that the hunter 'had been out searching for *Mormo*, or honey-bag, and had filled his *Numalka*, or dilly-bag, with it and was carrying it around his neck...and on his way back to camp came across a big black kangaroo. In some way he managed to get in front of it, and while it stood up quickly for a moment or two, to look round, he ran up and speared it' (ibid.: 810–11). Spencer was impressed with the 'really wonderful way in which the ...artist has depicted the pose that is always assumed by the animal when alarmed – the exact position of the body, the head thrown well up and slightly back, and the two little forelimbs held forward helplessly' (ibid.:810). Spencer was

equally impressed with the way the artist had expressed 'the relative proportions of the body and the accurate, if conventionalized delineation of the internal anatomy. Amongst the features he commented on was the backbone 'regarded as the main, strong support of the body, and to emphasize the strength of the hind limbs the femur is drawn in the same way as the backbone' (ibid.). The white configurations represent the abdomen and intestines and the rectangular shapes on either side of the spinal column indicate the animal's muscles.

ii.
JABIRU
Artist unknown
Group: Kakadu
Oenpelli, c.1912
96.5 x 61
Cahill Collection
Museum of Victoria

The jabiru was called *burtpenniweir* by the Kakadu. The bird is painted in two shades of red ochre and white pipeclay: the bird's long beak is painted in black.
(Houston 1965:cat.6)

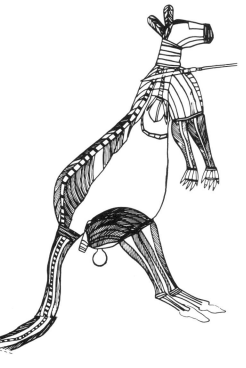

Rock painting
A male kangaroo in x-ray style
Deaf Adder Creek, Bala-Uru, Site 4
Brandl 1982:fig.166

iii.
TORTOISE AND FISH
Artist unknown
Group: Kakadu
Oenpelli, c.1912
82 x 20
Spencer Collection
Museum of Victoria

This superb *x-ray* painting depicts a freshwater tortoise and a fish called *burrameipa*.
(AAB 1979:145)

LIGHTNING SPIRIT
Artist unknown
Oenpelli, c.1912
142.5 x 61
Cahill Collection
Museum of Victoria

This painting has been described as a Lightning Spirit 'called *Nalupi, Namarvon*, or *Ngalura*, according to the particular tribe or moiety by whom he is commonly represented in bark paintings. The arm joints of the figure sprout axes for killing men and the oval composition represents the circumference and the cloud from which the lightning came' (Houston 1965:cat.2).
   Later representations of the Lightning Spirit bear a general formal relationship to this early painting. However significant variations in stylistic treatment, body designs as well as iconography are apparent (cf.cat.37–39; AAB 1979:86).

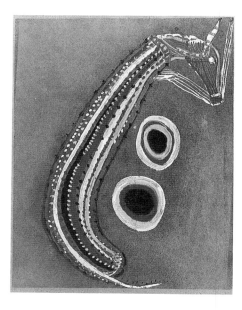

spherical stones belonging to Ngalyod's totemic places (cf.Mountford 1956:212). According to one of Brandl's artist informants, Jacky Bunggarnial, this painting was done by Mandarg at Oenpelli in 1948 (cf.Brandl 1982:181).
(Mountford 1956:212,pl.60B)

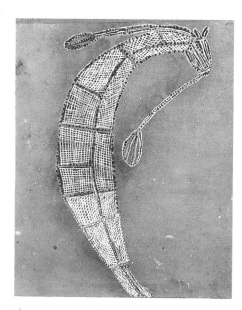

vi.
NGALYOD : THE RAINBOW SNAKE
Artist unknown
Oenpelli, c.1948
45 x 58.5
Mountford Collection
National Gallery of Victoria

The body of the Rainbow Snake, Ngalyod, is articulated into square and rectangular shapes with *rarrk* patterns. Mountford (1956:218) states that 'the appendage from his lower jaw is a long beard, and the one from behind his ears, a head ornament decorated with feathers.'
(Mountford 1956:218, pl.64B)

vii.
NGALYOD : THE RAINBOW SNAKE
Possibly by Mandarg
Gunei language group eastern Kunwinjku
Oenpelli, c.1948
45 x 58.2
Mountford Collection
National Gallery of Victoria

There is no underlying silhouette forming the basic shape of this image whose features are painted against the greenish-grey background of the paper. Ngalyod is shown with long whiskers and the circles on the right represent

iv.
GNORMO:A BENIFICENT SPIRIT
Artist unknown
Group: Geimbio
Oenpelli, c.1912
119.5 x 51
Spencer Collection
Museum of Victoria

According to Spencer, this painting depicts 'a gnome or sprite amongst the Geimbio tribe. It is one of a number to which the general term, Gnormo, is applied. It is supposed to fly around during the day or on moonlight nights, never during the dark. It rests amongst the Bamboo trees, hanging on by means of a special rope structure made from Banyan-tree bark. This is represented by the white lines' (Spencer 1922:129). Elsewhere, Spencer remarked that 'its general shape, except for the short tail, is rather suggestive of an opossum, which the natives see amongst the trees on moonlight nights. it is thickly covered with hair, called *Ngoinbu*, with very large hairy masses representing ears called *krabir*. The whole body is white. This particular spirit is friendly...if it sees a native ill, out in the bush, it goes in search of a medicine man, tells him to come and shows him the way' (Spencer 1928:807).
   The disposition of the figure and the object on which it is seated bear on interesting formal resemblance to Nabarrayal's portrayal of an Evil Spirit'. (cat.53).
(Spencer 1928:807, fig.524; Spencer 1922:129,fig.242)

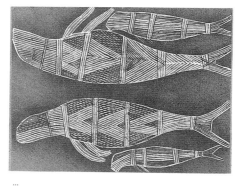

viii.
DUGONGS
by Wulkini
Country: Liverpool River Area)
Oenpelli, c.1948
46 x 58.5
Mountford Collection
National Gallery of Victoria

This painting, by an artist from the Liverpool River area, portrays a female dugong with her young. The dugong, a rare sea-mammal living in waters along the north coast of Australia, was fished by coastal Aborigines.
(Mountford 1956:14–15,242,pl.73A)

ix.
BANDICOOTS
Artist unknown
Oenpelli, c.1948
45.5 x 58.5
Mountford Collection
National Gallery of Victoria

This painting depicts two bandicoots – small, scrub dwelling marsupials. The x-ray details of

heart and lungs are shown slightly differently in each animal. There is also variation in the *rarrk* patterns on their bodies and the treatment of their faces and limbs. They are painted on paper in yellow, white and brown pigment.
(Mountford 1956:244;pl.74A)

x.
TJANGURA AND NARABA
Artist unknown
Oenpelli, c.1948
91 x 36
Mountford Collection
National Gallery of Victoria

This painting depicts Tjangura, the blue-tongued lizard and the gecko, Naraba (cf. Mountford 1956:213). The strong, geometric divisioning of the body, in particular the use of the x or cross motif as a central motif has its counterpart in recent Kunwinjku painting (cf.cat.1 &22). The extensive use of dots as infill patterns is more typical of mid-century Oenpelli paintings.
(Mountford 1956:213,pl.61c)

1.
NJALGAN : ARCHER FISH
by Namerredje Guymala
47 x 60

This beautifully patterned image of Njalgan is painted in the characteristic format of the *x-ray* style. The two main divisions on the upper part of each fish contain x-shaped motifs which visually link to form a strong, central diamond pattern. The dominant geometric treatment of the image and the tendency towards intense colour juxtapositions in the striped tail and gills are also to be seen in another of Namerredje's innovative paintings, Kalkberd : Euro (cat.23) – although other images of macropods by him (cat.22 & 59) are more conventional in colour and design.
  Njalgan is also known as the rifle fish because of its way of catching prey by spitting with great velocity at insects on low lying vegetation and eating them when they fall to the surface of the water. An image of Njalgan in the act of spitting at its prey, Gardap, the spider, is painted at Obiri Rock in Kakadu National Park.
(AAB 1977:cat.15)

2.
NAMARNKOL : BARRAMUNDI
by Spider Namirrkgi Nabunu
60 X 71

Namirrkgi's painting of barramundi, follows the conventions of the *x-ray* style, although it is not a static image but rather suggests movement and buoyancy. The *rarrk* patterns on each fish are finely executed and differ slightly. The larger fish shows some anatomical details which are not indicated in the smaller fish. It is possible that these differences reflect taxonomic distinctions. Kunwinjku speakers on the Mann River classify the barramundi by age – as immature, developed male, and sexually inverted, aged female (Altman, quoted in Gillespie 1982:17). There are many superb x-ray paintings of barramundi in the rock art of the Oenpelli-Kakadu region, reflecting its importance as a food source.
  Namarnkol, the Barramundi Ancestor spirit, is an important being in Kunwinjku mythology and is responsible for one of the major formations in the Kunwinjku landscape. A story tells of the creation of the East Alligator River by Namarnkol as he forced his way through the sandstone hills and across the plains to the ocean. Along the course of the East Alligator River, there are two Barramundi Dreaming sites. One is situated where the river emerges from the sandstone plateau at the place where the Barramundi went underground; the other, which lies approximately twenty kilometres downstream is located where the Barramundi reappeared after having created the course of the river across the black-soil plains and through the sandstone hills (AAB 1979:137). In

an eastern manifestation, Narmankol (also in fish shape) was trapped in shallow water and gradually hardened into rock (Berndt & Berndt 1970:27). This place is a sacred site which people are required to treat with respect and look after in ritually prescribed ways.
(AAB 1977:cat.14)

3.
NAWALAH : STINGRAYS
by Yuwunyuwun Marruwarr
82 x 51.5

The stingrays are painted in white, black and reddish ochre on a black background. The eyes and mouth, or 'face' of each stingray is enclosed within a heart-shaped motif. The diagonal rhythm of the *rarrk* patterning within the articulated areas results in an overall herringbone effect in the upper stingray whereas the patterning on the lower stingray forms a central diamond shape. The use of alternating 'bands' of colour formed by a very tight and regular cross-hatching technique results in strong, delicately painted diagonal patterns characteristic of Yuwunyuwun's personal style. An interesting comparison with his Nawalah is to be found in the Liverpool River painting of a stingray (c.1948) illustrated by Mountford (1956 pl.72D). In the earlier painting the articulated divisioning is based on a segmented circle and the dotted infill in the bounding lines is less formalized; the surface design on the body of the stingray consists of numerous sketchy dashes indicating the skin pattern.
(AAB 1977:cat.13; AAB 1979:143)

4.
THE FATE OF THE GREEDY FISHERMAN
by Bob Balirrbalirr Dirdi
54 x 39.5

The subject of this painting is a cautionary tale about a fisherman who caught more than his requirements. In their daily hunting, fishing and gathering pursuits, Aboriginal people sought to maintain the balance of nature and did not take more than they needed to survive. This painting graphically portrays the fate of an individual whose exploitative action represents a threat to the balance of nature. The fisherman, with spear and his catch of eighteen fish strung together beside him, is being drowned in the angry stranglehold of an octopus. His offence is imaged as a transgression against natural law, against a creature of the sea which he has overfished. Paintings of this kind, and the stories related to them played a part in the traditional education of young children.
(AAB 1977:cat 16; AAB 1979:103)

5.
KUMOKEN : CROCODILES
by Dick Nguleingulei Murrumurru
107 x 56

The artist has represented two Johnson River freshwater crocodiles in *x-ray* style in an image of great expressive character. Whilst the x-ray features dominate the design, the teeth and scaly back and tail of the crocodiles are also decoratively elaborated.
  There are two species of crocodile common in the Northern Territory. The freshwater crocodiles, or Kumoken, in Nguleingulei's painting can be identified by their long thin snouts. The saltwater crocodile has a short snout and thicker body; it grows much bigger and is dangerous to man.
  Myths relate how the crocodile, in the Dreaming, lived in the dry inland region and wanted to make his way to the sea. He

relentessley ate his way through the mountains to get there, creating the Liverpool Range (AAB 1977:26).
(AAB 1977:cat.12; AAB 1979:140)

6.
DADBE AND NGARDERRWO : TWO SNAKES AND A TORTOISE
by Dick Nguleingulei Murrumurru
68 x 53

There is a formal similarity between this painting and the previous one by Nguleingulei in his use of figure to frame the central space. In Dadbe and Ngarderrwo, his treatment of the snakes and tortoise creates an effect of power and elegance.
    The powerful movement of the snakes is suggested in compressed stylized rhythms and reinforced by the forceful x-ray portrayal of the backbone on the outside edge of their bodies. Interestingly, the artist has only cross-hatched the lower portion of one snake, leaving the rest of the infill pattern as very finely painted lines.
    Dadbe are brown snakes and are also known as Yirrbardbard in another Kunwinjku dialect. Yirrbardbard is an important being in Kunwinjku mythology and in his snake manifestation 'expresses hostility to everyone' (Berndt & Berndt 1970:154). These creatures inhabit the rocky sandstone escarpment.
(AAB 1977:cat.11; AAB 1979:138)

7.
KAWALAN : GOANNAS
by Lofty Nabarrayal Nadjamerrek
67.5 x 37

The artist has depicted male and female Kawalan: the larger one with tongue extended is the male. Goannas are a staple element in the Kunwinjku diet and are found in the sandstone terrain of western Arnhem Land. Kawalan, like other lizards, have the capacity to regenerate their tails should they be damaged and it appears that the two in this painting have met with an accident. The depiction of animals in broad areas of colour – a basic silhouette with small areas of fine patterning – against a black background is characteristic of this artist's personal style (cf. cat.8,13& 24). The faces of the Kawalan are interestingly treated; they show the x or cross motif which is common in Nabarrayal's paintings; their eyes, with optic nerve 'lines' attached connect to its centre. X-ray features are limited to the depiction of the backbone and the only other surface treatment consists of fine parallel lines painted on some triangular areas along the backs of the animal. The male Kawalan also bears the cross design on its legs.
    Kawalan is an important figure in Kunwinjku mythology and ceremonies.
(AAB 1977:cat.20; AAB 1979:120)

8.
DUKULA AND LAMBALK : POSSUMS FEEDING
by Lofty Nabarrayal Nadjamerrek
68 x 55.5

Nabarrayal has painted two possums, called Dukula, nibbling the new shoots of a young plant. In the top right hand corner Lambalk, the glider possum is portrayed. The use of whitish silhouettes incorporating fine monochrome patterns against a black background is a classic statement of Nabarrayal's individual approach to painting natural species.
(AAB 1977:cat.22; AAB 1979:119)

9.
HUNTER AND DEAD KANGAROO
by Lofty Nabarrayal Nadjamerrek
36 x 65

The artist has portrayed the hunter with spear, spearthrower and dilly bag alongside the kangaroo he has successsfully hunted. Its belly has been opened and its intestines drawn out in preparation for the cutting up and distribution of its meat. In traditional Kunwinjku society strict laws determine the allocation of different parts of a large animal amongst the hunter's family (cf. AAB 1979:107).
(AAB 1977:cat.8)

10.
NGARRBEK : ECHIDNA
by Dick Nguleingulei Murrumurru
53 x 45.5

This x-ray painting of an echidna features an unusual geometric net-like design. The echidna's spines and extended tongue are depicted.
    There is a Kunwinjku legend which recounts how Ngarrbek, the echidna, and Naluna, the tortoise, came to have their present day forms: 'One day the echidna asked the tortoise to look after her baby while she went off hunting for them. She was away such a long time that the tortoise became very hungry and ate the echidna's baby. When the echidna returned to camp and found out what had happened, the two began to fight. The echidna threw heavy rocks at the tortoise which, as they hit the tortoise, formed its hard shell. The tortoise, on the other hand, gathered bamboo spears which she threw at the echidna and which stuck to the echidna forming her bristly coat. The two then had a long talk, and decided that the tortoise would go off and live by the water and the echidna would live in the rocky country so that they would never meet.
    This story is typical of many of the stories told by the Aboriginal people. It recounts how the animals came to have their particular form, and where they live, so that it is in fact an elementary hunting lesson, and as such is part of the traditional teaching system' (AAB 1979:118).
(AAB 1977:cat.19; AAB 1979:118)

11.
NGARD : TORTOISE
by Anchor Barbuwa Wurrkgidj
58 x 41

There are four kinds of tortoise found in the Oenpelli area: 'the long-necked fresh water tortoise, called *ngalmangeyi*, and three kinds of short-necked tortoises called *ngard, waradjan,* and *biribirikalamba* ... As each species is associated with a different Dreamtime Ancestor Being, the artist always distinguishes carefully the actual species which he is depicting' (AAB 1979:135).
    The shell and body of this tortoise are articulated into numerous geometric shapes formed by dotted borders and infilled with *rarrk* patterns. These are painted in a relatively loose manner and are strongly directional within each segment.
(AAB 1977:cat.10)

12.
NAWARAN : ROCK PYTHON
by Yuwunyuwun Marruwarr
73 x 46

This arresting, iconic image of a python, in a coiled position with its flickering tongue extended, is an unusual departure from standard ways of representing snakes – more commonly portrayed elongated with cross-hatched patterns.
(AAB 1977:cat.17)

13.
NGURRUDU : EMU
by Lofty Nabarrayal Nadjamerrek
53 x 96.5

Nabarrayal's subject is a dead emu with its neck broken in preparation for cooking. The feathers of the emu are highly prized by the Kunwinjku and are used for ceremonial head-dresses and regalia (cf. AAB 1979:122).
(AAB 1977:cat.21; AAB 1979:122)

14.
BENUK : BUSH TURKEY
by Yuwunyuwun Marruwarr
56.4 x 64

Yuwunyuwun's representation of a bush turkey exploits the basic form of the bird in a conventionalized rhythmic image suggestive of arrested action.
    During ceremonies re-enacting the adventures of the Bush Turkey Ancestors in the Dreamtime, the dance of Benuk is performed; the dancers' bodies are painted in designs symbolizing the bird (cf. AAB 1977:28).
(AAB 1977:cat.18.)

15.
KARRBADA : LONG YAM
by Anchor Barbuwa Wurrkgidj
71 x 43

Karrbada, the long yam, grows plentifully in the fertile areas along the Liverpool and Alligator Rivers and is only one of many varieties of yam gathered by the Kunwinjku. Karrbada has a long branching tuber and vine-like foliage.
    Mountford (1956:pl.84 A,B) illustrates a painting of Karrbada which is stylistically similar to Barbuwa's as well as an abstract painting of the 'totemic place of the same yam, at Gunwakinin, near the Liverpool River (ibid.:256). Part of the latter design refers to rocks at this site which were yams in the creation times'. Because of its Dreaming associations, Karrbada is important in ceremonies and is the subject of body designs.
(AAB 1977:cat.23; AAB 1979:149)

16.
YAM
by Bob Balirrbalirr Dirdi
80 x 59

This relatively abstract image represents one of the yam species, possibly Karrbada, the long yam. The bottom left section resembles the tuber part of Karrbada (cat.15) and the rest of the image may be read as the snaking vine of the plant without its leaves shown. As yam plants lose their leaves during the dry season and regain them with the onset of the first monsoon rains, the plant has become an important symbol of seasonality for the Kunwinjku.
    The form of the yam resembles a representation of the same subject by the eastern Kunwinjku artist, Mandarg (Brandl 1982:fig.145 – see below).

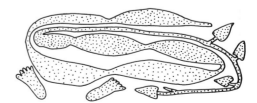

Brandl 1982: fig.145
drawing after a bark painting by Mandarg
A Long Yam and Human Footprints
Cadell River, 1969

17.
MANMARNAWAN : BUSH FRUIT
by Bob Balirrbalirr Dirdi
88 x 53.5

The bush, Manmarnawan, bears a small yellow fruit resembling a fig. The conventionalized naturalism of this painting provides an interesting comparison with Dirdi's more abstract treatment of the yam (cat.16). Manmarnawan:Bush Fruit bears an interesting formal resemblance to botanical drawings in the European tradition. Balirrbalirr's singular way of indicating the foliage by finely 'drawn' detail on the silhouetted form of the plant can also be seen in cat.42.
(AAB 1979:151)

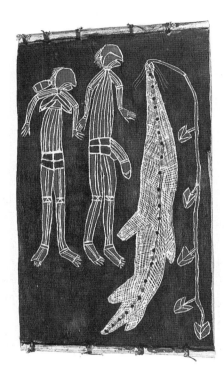

18.
MAN, WOMAN AND YAM
by Lofty Nabarrayal Nadjamerrek
49 x 28

It has been suggested that the man and woman in this painting are Mimi spirits (cf. AAB 1977:cat.52). The figures are reminiscent of earlier ways of portraying Mimi and other spirit people which show them with 'solid' bodies incorporating simple linear, x-ray and dotted designs (cf. Mountford 1956). Some of the more recent images of Mimi emphasize the thin and ethereal aspects of their physiognomy (cf. cat. 55).
   In the late 40s many of the Mimi were identified by name and their different ways of life known in detail: Mountford (1956:pl.54b) illustrates a painting of Mimi woman, Naluk, who lived in the jungle with her family and children; their diet consisted solely of the yams she collected. In this painting, the yam is also depicted in the foreground and painted much larger than the figure beside it — reflecting the symbolic conventions that generally apply to perspective in western Arnhem Land figurative art.
(AAB 1977:cat.52; AAB 1979:150)

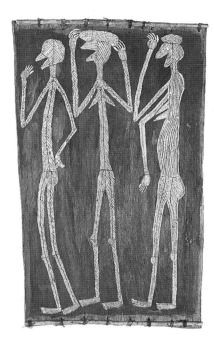

19.
RETURNING FROM FOOD GATHERING
by Bob Balirrbalirr Dirdi
87 x 50

Three figures are depicted: a man and his two wives carrying yam food on their heads. It has been suggested that these figures are either Mimi spirits or people (AAB 1979:104). Another possible interpretation of this subject is the story of Nabinkulawa and his two wives (cf. cat.36).
   The figures bear an interesting formal resemblance to a drawing after a rock painting illustrated in Mountford (1956:pl.47).
(AAB 1979:104)

20.
KOLOBARR: PLAINS KANGAROO
by Yuwunyuwun Marruwarr
89.5 x 55

Yuwunyuwun's painting of the male plains kangaroo, Kolobarr, includes x-ray features, such as heart, lungs and gut and extensive, tautly painted *rarrk* patterns. The sweeping upright position of the feet and tail is not found in earlier Oenpelli paintings in which it is more usual to show them beneath the animal, in a more 'naturalistic' position.
(AAB 1977:cat.1)

21.
KARURRKEN : PLAINS KANGAROO
by Yuwunyuwun Marruwarr
68.5 x 45.5

The Kunwinjku language distinguishes between different species of macropods and identifies the male and female of each species by separate names. Yuwunyuwun has here depicted the female plains kangaroo, Karurrken, with her joey.
(AAB 1977:cat.7)

22.
KOLOBARR : PLAINS KANGAROO
by Namerredje Guymala
89 x 33.5

The geometric x or cross design which was the central motif on the bodies of Namerredje's

Njalgon:Archer Fish (cat.1) is also the dominant design on the body of Kolobarr, the male plains kangaroo. Here, the motif is formed by dotted lines and *rarrk* patterns.
(AAB 1977:cat.3)

23.
KALKBERD : EURO
by Namerredje Guymala
88 x 42.5

Kalkberd is painted in a bold diamond and stripe design using broad areas of colour in striking juxtapositions. As it is difficult to identify taxonomic differences which would serve to differentiate Namerredje's portrayal of Kalkberd, a euro, from his Kolobarr, plains kangaroo (cat.22), it is possible, in this instance, that the body design itself signifies Kalkberd (cf.AAB 1979:p.67 , for a similar representation of Kalkberd with Ngalyod, the Rainbow Snake and Njanjmah, the native cat).
(AAB 1977:cat.2)

24.
KOLOBARR : PLAINS KANGAROO
by Lofty Nabarrayal Nadjamerrek
112 x 55

The relatively large scale of this painting invites comparison with early Oenpelli bark and rock paintings. There are other points of comparison, such as Nabarrayal's use of a 'classic' Kakadu palette: two shades of red ochre (one pink) and white although the black background is characteristic of his personal style. Certain patterns on the body of Kolobarr, such as the x design on the paws and the treatment of the neck and shoulders have parallels with the c.1912 painting of Madjiborla – the Black Kangaroo (cat.i).
(AAB 1977:cat.5)

25.
KOLOBARR : PLAINS KANGAROO
by Anchor Barbuwa Wurrkgidj
97 x 52

Barbuwa's Kolobarr is quite different from other images of the kangaroo in the exhibition. The

pose of the kangaroo and the artist's use of dots as infill designs is more typical of Oenpelli art of the late 40s illustrated in Mountford (1956). The geometric shapes which articulate the body are also to be seen on the face, without *rarrk* patterns, and add to the distinctive appearance of this kangaroo.
(AAB 1977:cat.4)

26.
KANDAKID : PLAINS KANGAROO
by Bob Balirrbalirr Dirdi,
90 x 69

Kandakid, the name for Kolobarr in another Kunwinjku dialect, is shown bent sideways, scratching his back. The entire body of the kangaroo is strikingly patterned, including the minimal x-ray features. An unusual use of colour, of black against yellow, and both with white against a pinkish-brown background, further distinguishes this exceptional painting.
   Kandakid is an important Dreaming figure and features in many Kunwinjku ceremonies.
(AAB 1977:cat.6)

27.
THREE RAINBOW SNAKES
by Fred Didjbaralkka Narroldol
86.5 x 62

Didjbaralkka has painted Ngalyod in three snake manifestations of awesome appearance and fierce expression – reflecting perhaps the fear in which the Rainbow Snake is held in its role as an agent of punishment and destruction.
(AAB 1977:cat.24)

28.
NGALYOD IN HER WATERHOLE
by Bob Wanurr Namundja
39 x 84

During the dry season, Ngalyod is said to inhabit deep billabongs and lagoons : waterlilies on the surface are said to indicate her presence. In the wet season, Ngalyod appears in the sky as a rainbow (Taylor 1984). Wanurr has represented Ngalyod in a characteristic guise but with a fish tail and fins and waterlilies along her back.
   The work, the only one of Wanurr's in the exhibition is most delicately painted: it is possible that the very fine stripes of colour on the waterlilies and parts of the body refer to Ngalyod's manifestation as the Rainbow.
(AAB 1977:cat.25; AAB 1979:66)

29.
NGALYOD
by Yuwunyuwun Marruwar
85 x 48

Ngalyod is represented in snake form with a characteristic head incorporating composite features – kangaroo ears, crocodile snout and teeth as well as a feathery 'antler-like' extension which in many versions of Ngalyod mythology is said to assist her in travelling underground.
(AAB 1977:cat.26)

30.
NGALYOD AND THE SACRED TREE
by Yuwunyuwun Marruwarr
62 x 68

This painting depicts the Rainbow Snake encircling a sacred tree and refers to Ngalyod's role as a protector of sacred sites. This portrayal is similar to cat.29 by Yuwunyuwun but also incorporates the chest bulge depicted in paintings of the emu and bush turkey (cf.cat.14) in its composite imagery.

74

31.
NGALYOD
by Lofty Nabarrayal Nadjamerrek
46.5 x 61

The artist has painted a superb and unusual visualization of Ngalyod, the Rainbow. Whilst the head of Ngalyod is a characteristic representation, kangaroo-like, with crocodile teeth, whiskers and 'antlers' (as they are commonly referred to in the literature) the body, to some extent, resembles a crocodile. The western Arnhem Land artist Mandarg described the 'antler' feature in one of his own paintings of the Rainbow Snake as *djaradjelina*, a head-dress of black cockatoo feathers which is twisted into the hair of performers in ceremonies (cf. Brandl 1983:1981). Elsewhere Brandl is quoted as likening the form of Nabarrayal's Ngalyod to rock art representations of the Tasmanian tiger (AAB 1979:61).
(AAB 1977:cat.27; AAB 1979:61)

32.
NGALYOD AND THE BIRDS
by Dick Nguleingulei Murrumurru
45 x 35

Nguleingulei's painting is about a Dreaming event in which Ngalyod was speared in the side by three men who wanted to release the fellow tribesmen she had swallowed. As Ngalyod was dying, she vomited forth all the people inside her including men, women and children. The three men were then transformed into birds – a kookaburra, a willy wagtail and a pee wee. Because of their heroic act in the Dreaming, these birds are not hunted today.
(AAB 1977:cat.28; AAB 1979:62)

33.
BORLUNG
by Paddy Nadamdjorle Maralngurra
62 x 36

Borlung is another name for the Rainbow and Brandl (1983:206) lists it as deriving from the Ngalgbon, Djauan and Maielli languages of western Arnhem Land. He remarks that the Rainbow 'is not a single being but several that are linked in genealogical order.' His artist informants talked of Jingana 'the Mother who existed at the beginning of time (*goregun*)...Jingana grew two large eggs in her body...from one of them emerged a son, Borlung, who had the body of a snake. The other egg contained a daughter, Ngalgunburijaimi who looked more like a fish.'

Brandl lists Jingana as a Ngalgbon and Rembarnga term for the ancestral mytho-totemic being, the Rainbow (ibid.). Brandl notes that 'while Jingana the Rainbow tends to be represented in paintings as a composite figure, Borlung, the Rainbow, is usually more snake-like in shape (ibid.:181). In Nadamdjorle's painting, Borlung is coiled around sacred objects.
(AAB 1977:cat.29)

34.
NGALYOD AND NGALKUNBURRIYAYMI
by Namerredje Guymala
83 x 57

In western Arnhem Land cosmology Ngalkunburriyaymi is a female spirit, daughter of the original creator being Jingana (cf.cat.33). In Namerredje's painting she is encircled by her brother, Ngalyod, the Rainbow; her body is patterned with ceremonial body designs.
(AAB 1977:cat.30)

35.
NGALKUNBURRIYAYMI : THE FEMALE SPIRIT
by Namerredje Guymala
59 x 44

This is a slightly different representation of Ngalkunburriyaymi by Namerredje, in which he shows her 'seated' on an object which symbolizes her sacred site.
(AAB 1977:cat.31)

36.
NABINKULAWA AND HIS TWO WIVES
by Sam Manggudja Ganarradj
50 x 28

This painting 'tells the story of Mirnaliwo, one of Nabinkulawa's wives, and is a warning to young wives to be faithful to their husbands who are often older men. Dire consequences befall young wives who have young sweethearts, and the story depicted by this bark tells of such an occurrence.
   The artist has portrayed the story of a man who lived long ago; he was called Nabinkulawa, and because he was a good hunter he was given a second wife, a young girl called Mirnaliwo. She was frightened of her husband and did not want to live with him. A number of years passed and Mirnaliwo became pregnant. Nabinkulawa knew the baby was not his as his young wife had a sweetheart. One day while they were all out looking for sugarbag, it started to rain, so Nabinkulawa built two shelters – one for him and his first wife and the other for Mirnaliwo.
   Nabinkulawa was a *marrkidjbu* or "clever man" with great powers and wanted to kill Mirnaliwo because of her sweetheart. He went into the bush near the camp and called upon Ngalyod, the Rainbow Serpent and instructed it to go and kill his young wife. The serpent was told to travel underground and to emerge inside Mirnaliwo's shelter and to eat her. The snake left Nabinkulawa and travelled underground to the shelter where it surfaced and swallowed Mirnaliwo head first. It went back underground and travelled towards the sandstone country where it emerged inside a cave and vomited her onto the wall of the cave. Today she is a rock painting and is a warning to all young wives.
   In a version of the *ubar* myth, Berndt records that Mirnaliwo (Minaliwu) is the wife of Jurawadbad (Yirawadbad) one of the mythical originators of the *ubar* ritual. Mirnaliwo is killed by Jurawadbad who emerges from a hollow log in the form of a snake and bites her, because she refused to accept her husband' (AAB 1979:81; cf. Berndt & Berndt 1970:119).
(AAB 1977:cat.32; AAB 1979:81)

37.
NAMARRKON : THE LIGHTNING SPIRIT
by Jimmy Nakkurridjdjilmi Nganjmira
59 x 29.5

Namarrkon 'is responsible for lightning and
thunder, which he produces by striking out with
the stone axes which protrude from his joints
   and   is painted on both bark and stone in a
form informants describe as "like a
grasshopper" ' (Gillespie 1982:18). Namarrkon
is said to have "made" *aljurr*, Leichardt's, or the
spectacular grasshopper (*Pelasida
ephippigera*). The species emerges, mates and
is most active and visible in the season known
as *gunemeleng*, between October and
December when there are intense electrical
storms. Aljurr is then said to be 'looking for'
Namarrkon, the lightning spirit' (ibid.).
   Nakkurridjdjilmi has painted the Lightning
Spirit in a characteristic guise. The lines
connecting his wrists and ankles represent
lightning flashes. A circuit of lightning encloses
his body passing through his head and
testicles. Stone axes are attached to his knees.
This representation suggests the sexual
connotations often associated with thunder and
lightning in Aboriginal mythology: 'In eastern
Arnhem Land the thunder man creates
lightning with his penis and Namarrkon, in the
west, appears with a circuit from head and
limbs to the testes' (AAB 1977:40).
   Mountford (1956:pls.59 B C,60A) illustrates
three paintings of the Lightning Spirit. In one of
these (60A) his form closely resembles that of a
grasshopper and he is portrayed 'lying across'
the sky.
(AAB 1977:cat.33; AAB 1979:83)

38.
NAMARRKON: THE LIGHTNING SPIRIT
by Jimmy Nakkurridjdjilmi Nganjmira
75 x 59

Considerable variations are to be seen in this
version of Namarrkon by Nakkurridjdjilmi
(cf. cat.37) – in the treatment of the face, the
body designs and the way in which the circuit
of lightning connects with the body.
   Namarrkon is believed to initiate 'severe
tropical electrical storms, which cause
widespread damage, destroying camps and
even killing people...it is widely held that the
marrkidjbu or "clever men" have the power to
call on the lightning man to strike a particular
person whom they wish to have killed'
(AAB 1979:82).
(AAB 1977:cat.34; AAB 1979:84)

39.
NAMARRKON : THE LIGHTNING SPIRIT,
AND THE WARDBUKARRA –
WARDBUKARRA
by Jimmy Nakkurridjdjilmi Nganjmira
30 x 54

This painting has previously been interpreted
as 'Lightning Spirit and Mimi Ceremony'
(cf. AAB 1979:85; AAB 1977:40) although Taylor
(pers. comm.) has suggested that it more
probably represents the same story as cat.40
(see below).
(AAB 1977:cat.35; AAB 1979:85)

40.
NAMARRKON : THE LIGHTNING SPIRIT AND
THE WARDBUKARRA – WARDBUKARRA
by Dick Nguleingulei Murrumurru
40 x 74

This painting concerns a story associated with
the artist's clan lands near Manmoyi outstation.
The people outside the cave are the
dangerous spirits Wardbukarra-Wardbukarra
who abducted the son of Lightning and took
him back to their cave where they proceeded

to sing and dance about their good fortune.
The boy escaped and found his father who
returned to the cave and hurled a lightning bolt
at it. The cave collapsed, trapping the
Wardbukarra-Wardbukarra inside (Taylor pers.
comm.). Namarrkon, shown above the cave, is
here portrayed in a form which differs from his
characteristic appearance as the Lightning
Spirit (cf.cat.37-39).

41. POSSUM, BANDICOOT AND GOANNA AT
THE SACRED ROCK
by Jimmy Nakkurridjdjilmi Nganjmira
46 x 70

In this painting, a possum, bandicoot and
goanna are depicted at an important site in
western Arnhem Land. The designs on the
rock are significant clan designs, the precise
meaning of which would not be divulged to the
uninitiated or to women (cf.AAB 1977:26). In
Aboriginal mythology, Ancestral Beings had the
power to change between animal and human
form. Many of these Beings underwent a final
metamorphosis, or became *djang*,
incorporating their sacred essence in specific
features of the natural landscape whose
formations they created in the course of their
Dreaming journeys. The rock in this painting
represents such a site and is a visible
manifestation of the eternal presence of the
Dreaming Ancestors.
(AAB 1977:cat.9)

42.
HUNTER AND DREAMING KANGAROO
by Bob Balirrbalirr Dirdi
69 x 38

This painting depicts a hunter who killed the
Dreaming Kangaroo at a particular site in
western Arnhem Land. The central section
represents the rocks at this site where the
Dreaming Kangaroo became *djang*, entering
the ground and investing the landscape with its
Dreaming potency. The style of the patterning
on the rocks refers to this power. The rocks at
this site are today respected as a visible
manifestation of the transformed Kangaroo
(Taylor. pers. comm.).
   The vegetation around the edges of the rock
formation is depicted in an unusually
naturalistic manner (cf.cat.17).

43.
KANGAROO PLAYING THE DIDJERIDU
by Lofty Nabarrayal Nadjamerrek
90.5 x 51 cm

This painting 'depicts a scene from the legend
associated with *Nadulmi*, the great Kangaroo of
the Dreamtime who found the first didjeridu
which belonged to the ancestral hero
Yirawadbad. It is now symbolized by the hollow
log drums used in the *Ubar* ceremonies of
western Arnhem Land' (AAB 1977:43).

44.
KUNBUDJURRI, CEREMONIAL LEADER OF
THE UBAR
by Fred Didjbaralkka Narroldol
56.5 x 22.5

The *Ubar* ceremony is one of the major
ceremonial cycles in western Arnhem Land: 'In
many dances and at different sites, the
activities of the Dreamtime ancestral hero,
Yirawadbad, are re-enacted. His didjeridu
became the hollow log now used as a sacred
drum in these ceremonies. The precise
meaning of this painting may not be divulged
to uninitiated men or women' (AAB 1977:40).
(AAB 1977:cat.36)

45.
LUMA LUMA
by Bobby Barrdjaray Nganjmira
64 x 55

In the Dreaming, Luma Luma came from the
east, travelling over the country that now
belongs to the Kunwinjku. He carried with him
sacred carved images of the barramundi,
mackerel and goanna. The myth of Luma
Luma forms the basis of the important *maraian*
ceremonies held by the Kunwinjku. In his
creative aspects, Luma Luma instituted
important ceremonies, dances and sacred
body designs (cf.AAB 1977:43). But he also
possessed powerful and terrifying aspects and
in one account was speared to death and 'his
spirit became a whale and swam out to sea'
(Berndt & Berndt 1970:122).
   Luma Luma is portrayed with two fish, a
barramundi and a Spanish mackerel
'recognizable because of the many small
spikes on its back and distinctive tail' (AAB
1977:43).
(AAB 1977 cat:38)

46.
LIKANAYA AT HER SACRED WATERHOLE
by Bobby Barrdjaray Nganjmira
56 x 31

This painting concerns the story of yowk yowk
(young girls). Yowk yowk paintings are

produced by a number of artists in western Arnhem Land. Two different pairs of yowk yowk sisters traversed a number of different clan lands in this area leaving their sacred essence at a number of sites (cf.Taylor 1984). This yowk yowk painting depicts Likanaya, sister of Marrayka, at her sacred waterhole, Indjularrku, in the Gumaderr River area (AAB 1979:69). Nadjalama clan artists of the Nganjmira family are considered owners of this site and paint the story frequently. Another painting of Likanaya by Bobby Barrdjaray Nganjmira, and one of both sisters by Jimmy Nakkurridjdjilmi Nganjmira, are illustrated in *Oenpelli Bark Paintings* (AAB 1979:70-71). Taylor (ibid.) gives the yowk yowk story as follows: 'Two sisters, who had been collecting food near a deep waterhole attempt to cook the food too near the waterhole and anger the Rainbow Serpent who rises from the billabong and tries to kill them. The girls are forced to dive into the billabong and there they remain as Dreaming to this day'.

This image of Likanaya is one of the more common representations showing her as a mermaid-like figure. She has a dilly bag suspended from her head and holds a feathered string in one hand. Images of Likanaya may vary widely from this one and include elements signifying her other manifestations as waterweed, insects and beetles associated with the billabong. Some representations incorporate geometric circles which represent the billabongs associated with the myth and this painting has been interpreted as showing the river crossing between them (cf.the tail and torso section of her body). A series of paintings on this theme may be seen as a map of the Dreaming associations of Gundjalama country (cf.Taylor:ibid.).
(AAB 1977:cat.39; AAB 1979:69)

47.
NGALDJORLBOH, THE SPIRIT WOMAN
by Bobby Barrdjaray Nganjmira
59 x 39

Ngaldjorlboh, a woman of the Dreaming, has been gathering food. A filled dilly bag is suspended from her head and another from the branch of a tree. Berndt and Berndt (1970:121) write that women sometimes refer to Ngaldjorlboh, as the Creator Woman of the *Ubar* rituals.
(AAB 1979:101)

48.
NAMORRORDRDO SPIRITS
by Namerredje Guymala
68 x 42

This painting portrays the malicious spirits, Namorrordrdo, carrying their fighting sticks called *miyarru*. Their beards symbolize their magical power. They are said to roam about whistling in the night waiting to steal the souls of people who are lost. Shooting stars are another manifestation of Namorrordrdo – when people see one they say that these spirits have taken another soul (Taylor pers. comm.).

49.
NAWONGBERD AND HIS FOUR WIVES
by Dick Nguleingulei Murrumurru
49 x 85

Nawongberd, a devil spirit, is shown with his four wives at their camp site. They have returned from gathering food and their catch is lying on the ground. One of the women is depicted lying down and another, on the left of the painting, is shown in a manner unusual in Kunwinjku art: the bottom half of her torso is depicted in profile so that she appears to have only one leg. Lily roots are tucked into her string girdle. Nawongberd is associated with the Mangkodjbang Lily-Dreaming site near Oenpelli (cf.AAB 1979:72).
(AAB 1977:cat.42; AAB 1979:72)

50.
WAYARRA : EVIL SPIRITS AND KULUBAN:FLYING FOXES IN THEIR CAVE
by Anchor Barbuwa Wurrkgidj
68 x 61

The caves and crevices of the rocky escarpment are believed to be the dwelling places of various spirit creatures. In the upper part of the painting, the arched ceiling of the cave and three evil Wayarra spirits are depicted. Sharing it with them are flying foxes, resting suspended upside-down. The two dotted circles represent fires on the floor of the cave.
(AAB 1977:cat.41; AAB 1979:126)

51.
WAKEWAKEN SPIRIT
by Lofty Nabarrayal Nadjamerrek
49 x 27

The subject of this painting is an evil female Dreamtime spirit, called Wakewaken who is associated with a special site in the sandstone plateau near Oenpelli. At this place, there is dense growth of trees which bear a fruit called *nganwok*.
(AAB 1977:cat.40; AAB 1979:77)

52.
EVIL SPIRIT OR DEVIL
by Lofty Nabarrayal Nadjamerrek
60 x 37.5

This evil spirit is associated with a site called Dulklorrkelorrkeng and the object on which he is seated is a visual representation of this place. On the feet, hands and tongue of this figure is an x or cross motif which appears frequently in Nabarrayal's paintings. It has been suggested that the protruding tongue indicates that this spirit is engaged in some evil action (AAB 1979:78) and that this motif is often a feature of sorcery images (cf.AAB 1977:46).
(AAB 1977:cat.43; AAB 1979:78)

53.
EVIL SPIRIT OR DEVIL
by Lofty Nabarrayal Nadjamerrek
80 x 40

This is another painting of the Devil Dreaming at Dulklorrkelorrkeng on the artist's clan lands. Nabarrayal often paints this figure seated on a rock formation at the site.

He has included Nawaran, the rock python who is also associated with the site. The pattern on the rocks represents their Dreaming power (Taylor pers. comm.). This painting makes an interesting comparison with cat.iv.

54.
MALE AND FEMALE MIMI SPIRITS
by Jimmy Nakkurridjdjilmi Nganjmira
84.5 x 34

Nakkurridjdjilmi's portrayal of two Mimi spirits bears an interesting resemblance to ancient rock art figures classified as *mimi* style – examples of which are illustrated in Brandl (1983). His figure 144 represents an anthromorphic being akin to Nganjmira's 'kangaroo headed' (?) female Mimi. Figure 123 represents a human with x-ray features in the *mimi* style. The general disposition of the latter figure; the depiction of joint marks and central divisioning within the body; and the representation in profile of eyes with optic nerve lines have stylistic counterparts in Nakkurridjdjilmi's Mimi spirits. The male Mimi wears a feather head-dress.
(AAB 1977 cat.44; AAB 1979:90)

Brandl 1983: fig.123
Rock Painting
A human being with x-ray features
Mimi Art
Cadell River

Brandl 1983: fig.144
Rock Painting
A bisexual figure with the head of an animal
Near Cahill's Crossing on the East Alligator
River

55.
DANCING MIMI SPIRIT
by Dick Nguleingulei Murrumurru
60.5 x 32.5

Dancing is one of many arts that Mimi spirits
are said to have taught Aboriginal people. This
image has its counterparts, both in appearance
and lively energy. in the dynamic figure style of
ancient rock art. Mimi spirits have been
described as thin, delicate creatures and this
image portrays such a physiognomy. This
dancing Mimi, carrying a dilly bag suspended
from the head, is bisexual and appears to be
pregnant. The Mimi is painted in fine white
lines on a natural bark background.
(AAB 1977 cat.50)

56.
MIMI SPIRITS
by Anchor Barbuwa Wurrkgidj
41 x 27

Barbuwa's art generally, and his manner of
portraying Mimi relates more to the style of
Oenpelli paintings of the late 40s than the
majority of later works to be seen in the
exhibition (cf.cat.25). The Mimis' 'sexual
adventures were renowned and one story
relates that if a man or woman should wander
into the *Mimis'* camp and have intercourse with
one of them, he or she would change into a
Mimi spirit' (AAB 1977:33). The artist has
depicted two male Mimi spirits engaged in
sexual play.
(AAB 1977:51; AAB 1979:92)

57.
MIMI SPIRIT AND KANGAROO DANCING
by Spider Namirrkgi Nabunu
78.5 x 37

Both Mimi spirit and the Kangaroo with its joey
are engaged in a lively dance. The rhythm and
movement of the dance is superbly conveyed
through the positioning of the figures, and
particularly through the action and blown-back
head-dress of the Mimi.
(AAB 1977:cat.49)

58.
MIMI HUNTER AND FEEDING KANGAROO
by Spider Namirrkgi Nabunu
76 x 48

In a superb and dramatic composition
Namirrkgi has portrayed a Mimi hunter poised
to strike a kangaroo turned aside from feeding.
The artist has used unusual colours and
combinations to great effect, notably the red
and greenish-yellow ochres on the body of the
Mimi. The x-ray features of the kangaroo are
rendered in pink and the tail is boldly painted
in thin stripes in black, yellow and pink. The
figures are set against a dramatic black
background.
(AAB 1977:cat.48)

59.
MIMI HUNTER AND KANGAROO
by Namerredje Guymala
86 x 40

A wide range of Mimi themes are painted by
Kunwinjku artists. The story associated with this
painting concerns Nadulmi, the Dreaming
Kangaroo, an important figure in the *Ubar*
ceremonies (cf.AAB 1977:47).
(AAB 1977:cat.46)

60.
MIMI HUNTING THE KANGAROOS,
KOLOBARR AND KARURRKEN
by Dick Nguleingulei Murrumurru
112 x 53

The Mimi hunter is portrayed in a manner
reminiscent of the *mimi* human figure style of
ancient rock art. The hunter is poised to throw
the spear held in his woomera or spearthrower. A dilly bag is slung over his shoulder
and he carries a second spear. Subtle
differences in the patterns on the bodies of the
kangaroos are particularly evident in the x-ray
features which the artist has treated in a very
decorative manner. The figures are painted in
pale yellow ochre on a natural background –
cf.cat.49 by the same artist.
(AAB 1977 cat.45; AAB 1979:93)

ARTISTS' BIOGRAPHIES

Sam Manggudja Ganarradj b.1909
Group: Kunwinjku
Subsection: Nakangila
Clan: Namayirrkulidj
Country: Gumaderr River Area
Catalogue: 36

Bobby Barrdjaray Nganjmira b.1915
Group: Kunwinjku
Subsection: Nawakadj
Clan: Nadjalama
Country: Malwan, between Gudamerr and Liverpool
Rivers
Catalogue: 45, 46, 47

Dick Nguleingulei Murrumurru b.1920
Group: Kunwinjku
Subsection: Nawakadj
Clan: Nabularlhdja
Country: Kukadjerri, Liverpool River Plateau
Catalogue: 5, 6, 10, 32, 40, 49, 55, 60

Fred Didjbaralkka Narroldol b.1924
Group: Kunwinjku
Subsection: Nabangardi
Clan: Nadjok
Country: Ngolwarre, south of Maningrida
Catalogue: 27, 44

Lofty Nabarrayal Nadjamerrek b.1926
Group: Kunwinjku
Subsection: Nakodjok
Clan: Namok
Country: Mann River Plateau
Catalogue: 7, 8, 9, 13, 18, 24, 31, 43, 51, 52, 53

Bob Wanurr Namundja b.1933
Group: Kunwinjku
Subsection: Nawakadj
Clan: Nakardbam
Country: Arnhem Land Plateau
Catalogue: 28

Bob Balirrbalirr Dirdi (1905–77)
Group: Kunwinjku
Subsection: Nakangila
Clan: Nabarrbinj
Country: Marrkolidjban
Catalogue: 4, 16, 17, 19, 26, 42

Paddy Nadamjorle Maralngurra (1906–74)
Group: Kunwinjku
Subsection: Nakangila
Clan: Nangalngbali
Country: Gudamerr Plateau
Catalogue: 33

Jimmy Nakkurridjdjilmi Nganjmira (1917–82)
Group: Kunwinjku
Subsection: Nawakadj
Clan: Nadjalama
Country: Malwan, Yelerlban
Catalogue: 37, 38, 39, 41, 54

Spider Namirrkgi Nabunu (1924–73)
Group: Kunwinjku
Subsection: Nawamud
Clan: Nabularlhdja
Country: Arnhem Land Plateau
Catalogue: 2, 57, 58

Anchor Barbuwa Wurrkgidj (1924–77)
Group: Kunwinjku
Subsection: Nabulaj
Clan: Nakurulk
Country: Mumega
Catalogue: 11, 15, 25, 50, 56

Namerredje Guymala (1926–76)
Group: Kunwinjku
Subsection: Nangarridj
Clan: Naburdo
Country: Liverpool River Escarpment
Catalogue: 1, 22, 23, 34, 35, 48, 59

Yuwunyuwun Marruwarr (1928–78)
Group: Kunwinjku
Subsection: Nakamarrang
Clan: Namarrirn
Country: Liverpool River
Catalogue: 3, 12, 14, 20, 21, 29, 30

BIBLIOGRAPHY

BOOKS

Aboriginal Arts Board. *Oenpelli Bark Painting*. Ure Smith, Sydney, 1979.
The Aboriginal Children's History of Australia (illustrated by Aboriginal children). Rigby, Adelaide, 1977.
Adam, Leonard, *Primitive Art*. edn, rev. Pelican, 1949.
Allen, Louis A. *Time Before Morning; Art and Myth of the Australian Aborigines*. Rigby, Adelaide, 1976.
Attenborough, David. *Quest under Capricorn*. Lutterworth, London, 1963.
Berndt, Ronald M. (ed.). *Australian Aboriginal Art*. Ure Smith, Sydney, 1964.
Berndt, Ronald M. *The Sacred Site: The Western Arnhem Land Example*. Australian Institute of Aboriginal Studies, Canberra, 1970.
Berndt, Ronald M. *The Australian Aboriginal Heritage: An Introduction through the Arts*. Ure Smith, Sydney, 1973.
Berndt, Ronald M. *Australian Aboriginal Religion*. Brill, Leiden, 1974.
Berndt, Ronald, M. *Love Songs of Arnhem Land*. Nelson, Melbourne, 1976.
Berndt, Ronald M. & Berndt, Catherine H. *Sexual Behaviour in Western Arnhem Land*. Viking Fund Publications in Anthropology, no. 16. Viking Fund, N.Y., 1951.
Berndt, Ronald M. & Berndt, Catherine H. *Arnhem Land: Its History and Its People*. Cheshire, Melbourne, 1954.
Berndt, Ronald M. & Berndt, Catherine H. *The World of the First Australians*. Ure Smith, Sydney, 1964.
Berndt, Ronald M. & Berndt, Catherine H. (eds). *Aboriginal Man in Australia*. Angus and Robertson, Sydney, 1965.
Berndt, Ronald M. & Berndt, Catherine H. *Man, land and myth in North Australia: the Gunwinggu people*. Ure Smith, Sydney, 1970.
Berndt, Ronald M. & Berndt, Catherine H. *The World of the First Australians*. Rev. edn. Lansdowne Press, Sydney, 1981.
Berndt, Ronald M. & Berndt, Catherine H. & Stanton, John E. *Australian Aboriginal Art: A Visual Perspective*. Methuen, Sydney, 1982.
Berndt, Ronald M & Phillips, E. S. (eds). *The Australian Aboriginal Heritage: An introduction through the arts*. Australian Society for Education through the Arts in association with Ure Smith, Sydney, 1973.
Berndt, Ronald M. & Stanton, John E. *Australian Aboriginal Art in the Anthropology Museum of the University of Western Australia*. University of Western Australia Press, Perth, 1980.
Biebuyck, Daniel P. (ed.). *Tradition and Creativity in Tribal Art*. University of California Press, California, 1973.
Brandl, Eric J. *Australian Aboriginal Paintings in Western and Central Arnhem Land; Temporal sequences and elements of style in Cadell River and Deaf Adder Creek Art*. New Series no. 35. Reprinted with amendments. Australian Institute of Aboriginal Studies, Canberra, 1982.
Chaloupka, George. *Burrunguy-Nourlangie Rock*. Northart [1983]. (Chaloupka b).
Charlesworth, Max (ed.). *Religion in Aboriginal Australia: An Anthology*. UQP, Brisbane, 1984.
Cole, E. K. *A History of Oenpelli*. Nungalinya Publications, Darwin, 1975.
Dashwood, C. J. *Government Resident report on the Northern Territory*. 1897.
Edwards, Robert (ed.). *The Preservation of Australia's Aboriginal Heritage: A Report of the National Seminar on Aboriginal Antiquities in Australia May 1972*. Australian Aboriginal Studies no. 54. Australian Institute of Aboriginal Studies, Canberra, 1975.
Edwards, Robert (ed.). *Aboriginal Art in Australia*. Aboriginal Arts Board, Australia Council, Sydney, 1978.
Edwards, Robert. *Australian Aboriginal art: the art of the Alligator Rivers region, Northern Territory*. Australian Institute of Aboriginal Studies, Canberra, 1979.
Edwards, Robert & Guerin, Bruce. *Aboriginal Bark Paintings*. Rigby, Adelaide, 1969.
Eliade, Mircea. *Australian Religions: An Introduction*. Cornell University Press, New York, 1973.
Elkin, A. P. & Berndt, Ronald M. & Berndt, Catherine H. *Art in Arnhem Land*, Cheshire, Melbourne, 1950.
Forge, Anthony (ed.). *Primtive Art and Society*. Oxford University Press, London, 1973.
Gillespie, Dan (comp.). *The Rock Art sites of Kakadu National Park: Some Preliminary Research Findings for their Conservation and Management*. Special Publication 10. Australian National Parks and Wildlife, 1983.
Greenhalgh, Michael & Megaw, Vincent (eds). *Art in Society*. Duckworth, London, 1978.
Holmes, Sandra le Brun. *Yirawala: Artist and Man*. Jacaranda Press, Brisbane, 1972.
Honour, Hugh & Fleming, John. *A World History of Art*. Macmillan, London, 1982.
Isaacs, Jennifer (comp.). *Australian Dreaming: 40,000 years of Aboriginal History*. Lansdowne Press, Sydney, 1980.
Isaacs, Jennifer. *Arts of the Dreaming: Australia's Living Heritage*. Lansdowne Press, Sydney, 1984.
Jones, Rhys (ed.). *Northern Australia: Options and Implications*. Research School of Pacific Studies, ANU, Canberra, 1980.
Kupka, Karel. *The Dawn of Art: Painting and Sculpture of the Australian Aborigines*. Angus & Robertson, Sydney, 1965.
Leichhardt, Ludwig. *Journal of an Overland Expedition in Australia, from Moreton Bay to Port Essington*. T. and W. Boon, London, 1847.

Loveday, Peter & Cooke, Peter. *Aboriginal Arts and Crafts and the Market*. ANU North Australia Research Unit Monograph. Darwin, 1983.
McCarthy, Frederick D. *Australian Aboriginal Rock Art*. Australian Museum, Sydney, 196?.
McCarthy, Frederick D. *Australian Aboriginal Decorative Art*. 8 edns. Australian Museum, Sydney, 1974.
Mountford, Charles P. *Australia: Aboriginal Paintings – Arnhem Land*. UNESCO World Art Series. N.Y. Graphic Society, New York, 1954.
Mountford, Charles P. *Art, Myth and Symbolism-Records of the American-Australian Scientific Expedition to Arnhem Land*. Vol. 1, Melbourne University Press, Melbourne, 1956.
Mountford, Charles P. *Aboriginal Art*. Longmans, 1961.
Mountford, Charles P. & Roberts, Ainslie. *The Dawn of Time: Australian Aboriginal Myths in Paintings*. Rigby, Adelaide, 1969. Reprinted 1980.
Mulvaney, D. John. *Prehistory of Australia*. Thames and Hudson, London, 1969.
Mulvaney, D. John & Golson, J. (eds). *Aboriginal Man and Environment in Australia*. Australian National University Press, Canberra, 1971.
National Museum of Victoria. *Australian Aboriginal Art*. National Museum, Melbourne, 1929.
Spencer, Sir W. Baldwin & Gillen, F. J. *Native Tribes of the Northern Territory*. Macmillan, London, 1914.
Spencer, Sir W. Baldwin. *Wanderings in Wild Australia*. Vol. II. Macmillan, London, 1928.
Tatz, Colin. *Aborigines, Uranium and Other Essays*. Heinemann, Melbourne, 1982.
Ucko, Peter J. (ed.). *Form in Indigenous Art*. Australian Institute of Aboriginal Studies, Canberra, 1977.

EXHIBITION CATALOGUES

Aboriginal Arts Board. *Oenpelli Paintings on Bark*. Australian Gallery Directors' Council, 1977.
Aboriginal Arts Board. *Aboriginal Art of North Australia*. Australia Council, Sydney, n.d.
Allen, Louis A. *Australian Aboriginal Art: Arnhem Land*. Field Museum of Natural History, Field Museum Press, 1972.
Australian Museum. *Renewing the Dreaming*. Australian Museum, Sydney, 1977.
Berndt, Ronald M. & Berndt, Catherine H. *An Exhibition of Australian Aboriginal Art: Arnhem Land Paintings on Bark and Carved Human Figures*. Perth, 1957.
Carrick, John (ed.). *Art of the First Australians*. Australia Council, n.d.
Cooke, Peter & Altman, Jon. *Aboriginal Art at the Top*. A regional exhibition. Maningrida Arts and Crafts, N.T., 1982.
Cooper, Carol et al. *Aboriginal Australia*. Australian Gallery Directors' Council, 1981.
Houston. Museum of Fine Arts. *Aboriginal Bark Paintings from Australia: Aboriginal Bark Paintings from the Cahill and Chaseling Collection, National Museum of Victoria, Melbourne, Australia*. Museum of Fine Arts, Houston, Texas, 1965.
Norton, Frank. *Aboriginal Art: The Western Australian Art Gallery Collection*. Western Australian Art Gallery Board, 1969.
Spencer, Sir W. Baldwin. *A Guide to the Australian Ethnographical Collection*. Exhibited in the National Museum of Victoria, 1922.
State Art Galleries of Australia. *Bark Paintings, Carved Figures, Sacred and Secular Objects: Australian Aboriginal Art*. An exhibition arranged by the State Art Galleries of Australia, 1960-61.
Walker Art Gallery, Liverpool. *Australian Aboriginal Bark Paintings 1912-1964*. Commonwealth Arts Festival Exhibition organized by the Australian Institute of Aboriginal Studies Canberra. Walker Art Gallery Liverpool, 1965.

ARTICLES

Altman, John. 'Artists and Artisans in Gunwinggu Society'. In Cooke, P. & Altman, J. (eds), 1982, pp. 12-16.
Arndt, W. 'The Interpretation of the Delamere Lightning Paintings and Rock Engravings'. *Oceania* 32, 3, 1962, pp. 163-77.
Arndt, W. 'The Nargorkun-Narlinji Cult'. *Oceania* 32 4, 1962, pp. 288-320.
Australian Aboriginal Art. Special Number. *Art and Australia* 13, 3, summer, Jan.-Mar. 1976.
Berndt, Ronald M. 'Aboriginal Ochre-moulded Heads from Western Arnhem Land'. *Meanjin* x, 1952.
Berndt, Ronald M. 'The Mountford Volume on Arhhem Land Art'. *Mankind* 5, 6, 1958.
Berndt, Ronald M. 'Some Methodological Considerations in the Study of Australian Aboriginal Art'. In Jopling, Carol F. (ed.). *Art and Aesthetics in Primitive Societies: A Critical Anthology*. New York, 1971.
Berndt, Ronald M. 'The Changing Face of the Aboriginal Arts'. *Anthropological Forum* 111, 2, 1972.
Berndt, Ronald M. 'A Living Aboriginal Art: The Changing Inside and Outside Contexts'. In Loveday, P. (ed.), 1983.

Berndt, Ronald M. & Berndt, Catherine H. 'An Oenpelli Monologue: Culture Contact'. *Oceania* 22, 1, 1951, pp. 24-52.

Brandl, Eric J. 'Aboriginal Rock Designs in Beeswax and Description of Cave Painting Sites in Western Arnhem Land'. *Archaeology and Physical Anthropology in Oceania* 3, 1, 1968, pp. 19-29.

Carrington, F. 'The Rivers of the Northern Territory of South Australia'. In *Proceedings of the Royal Geographical Society* (S.A.), vol. 2, 1888.

Carroll, Peter J. 'Mimi from Western Arnhem Land'. In P. J. Ucko (ed.), 1977.

Carroll, Peter J. 'Aboriginal Art from Western Arnhem Land'. In Loveday, P. & Cooke, P. (eds), 1983.

Catalano, Gary. 'Changing Responses to Aboriginal Art'. *Meanjin* 36, 4, pp.572-81.

Chaloupka, George. 'Art in Situ'. In Loveday, P. & Cooke, P. (eds) 1983.

Chaloupka, George. 'Kakadu Rock Art: Its Cultural, Historic and Prehistoric Significance'. In Gillespie, D. (comp.), 1983. (Chaloupka a).

Elkin, A. P. 'Art and Life'. In Berndt, R. (ed.), 1964.

Foelsche, P. 'Notes on the Aborigines of North Australia'. In *Transactions of the Royal Society of South Australia*, vol. 5, 1882.

Fox, Steve. 'Quality is Not a Smooth Straight Line'. In Cooke, P. & Altman, J. (eds), 1982.

Gillespie, Dan. 'The Artist as Scientist'. In Cooke, P. & Altman, J. (eds), 1982, pp. 17-20.

Keen, Ian. 'The Alligator Rivers Aborigines – Retrospect and Prospect'. In Jones, R. (ed.), 1980.

Maddock, Kenneth. 'Imagery and Social Structure at Two Dalabon Rock Art Sites'. *Anthropological Forum* 2, 4, pp. 444-63.

McCarthy, Frederick D. 'The Art of the Rock Faces'. In Berndt, R. (ed.), 1964.

Mountford, Charles P. 'The Lightning Man in Australian Mythology'. *Man* 55, 1955, pp. 129-30.

Mountford, Charles P. 'Aboriginal Bark Paintings from Field Island, Northern Territory'. *South Australian Museum Records* 13, 1, 1957, pp. 87-9.

Mountford, Charles P. 'The Art of Arnhem Land'. In Berndt, R. (ed.), 1964, pp. 20-32.

Mountford, Charles P. 'The Aboriginal Art of Australia'. In Buhler, Alfred. *Oceania and Australia: The Art of the South Seas*. Methuen, London, 1965.

Morphy, Howard. 'The Art of Northern Australia'. In Cooper, Carol et al., 1981, pp. 53-65.

Taylor, Luke. 'Dreaming Transformations in Gunwinggu Bark Paintings'. M.S. Paper read to A.I.A.S. Biennial Conference *Aboriginal Arts in Contemporary Australia*, Australian National Gallery, May, 1984.

Tindale, Norman B. 'Native Rock Shelters at Oenpelli, Van Dieman's Gulf, North Australia'. *South Australian Naturalist* 9, 2, 1928, pp. 35-6.

Walston, Sue. 'Rock Art Deterioration and Conservation'. In Edwards, R. (ed.), 1975.

White, C. & Peterson, N. 'Ethnographic Interpretation of the Prehistory of Western Arnhem Land'. *Southwestern Journal of Anthropology* 25, 1, 1969, pp. 45-67.